Verbal
Reasoning
& Comprehension

The 11+
10-Minute Tests

For the CEM (Durham University) test

Ages
9-10

Practise • Prepare • Pass
Everything your child needs for 11+ success

How to use this book

This book is made up of 10-minute tests and puzzle pages.
There are answers and detailed explanations in the pull-out section at the back of the book.

10-Minute Tests

*   There are 31 tests in this book, each containing either 20 or 26 questions.

*   Each test is designed to cover a good range of the question styles and topics that your
    child could come across in the Verbal Reasoning sections of their 11+ test.

*   Your child should aim to score around 17 out of 20 or 22 out of 26 in each of the 10-minute tests.
    If they score less than this, use their results to work out the areas they need more practice on.

*   If your child hasn't managed to finish the test in time, they need to work on increasing their
    speed, whereas if they have made a lot of mistakes, they need to work more carefully.

*   Keep track of your child's scores using the progress chart on the inside back cover of the book.

Puzzle Pages

*   There are 10 puzzle pages in this book, which are a great break from test-style questions.
    They encourage children to practise the same skills that they will need in the test, but in a fun way.

Published by CGP

Editors:
Izzy Bowen, Holly Poynton and Sean Walsh

With thanks to Claire Boulter and Alison Griffin for the proofreading.

Please note that CGP is not associated with CEM or The University of Durham in any way.
This book does not include any official questions and it is not endorsed by CEM or The University of Durham.
CEM, Centre for Evaluation and Monitoring, Durham University and *The University of Durham*
are all trademarks of The University of Durham.

ISBN: 978 1 78294 626 7
Printed by Elanders Ltd, Newcastle upon Tyne
Clipart from Corel®

Based on the classic CGP style created by Richard Parsons.

Contents

You have **10 minutes** to do this test. Work as quickly and accurately as you can.

> Read this passage carefully and answer the questions that follow.

An extract from 'A Little Princess'

Once on a dark winter's day, when the yellow fog hung so thick and heavy in the streets of London that the lamps were lighted and the shop windows blazed with gas as they do at night, an odd-looking little girl sat in a cab with her father and was driven rather slowly through the big thoroughfares*.

5   She sat with her feet tucked under her, and leaned against her father, who held her in his arm, as she stared out of the window at the passing people with a queer old-fashioned thoughtfulness in her big eyes.

She was such a little girl that one did not expect to see such a look on her small face. It would have been an old look for a child of twelve, and Sara Crewe was

10   only seven. The fact was, however, that she was always dreaming and thinking odd things and could not herself remember any time when she had not been thinking things about grown-up people and the world they belonged to. She felt as if she had lived a long, long time.

At this moment she was remembering the voyage she had just made from

15   Bombay with her father, Captain Crewe. She was thinking of the big ship, of the Lascars** passing silently to and fro on it, of the children playing about on the hot deck, and of some young officers' wives who used to try to make her talk to them and laugh at the things she said.

Principally, she was thinking of what a queer thing it was that at one time one

20   was in India in the blazing sun, and then in the middle of the ocean, and then driving in a strange vehicle through strange streets where the day was as dark as the night. She found this so puzzling that she moved closer to her father.

Frances Hodgson Burnett

* thoroughfares — *main roads*
** Lascars — *sailors from India or Southeast Asia*

Answer these questions about the text that you've just read.
Circle the letter that matches the correct answer.

1. What information is not given in the passage?

   A   What season it is

   B   What the weather is like

   C   The name of Sara's mother

   D   Sara's age

2. What does the narrator say is surprising about Sara?

   A   Her unusually large eyes

   B   The serious look in her eyes

   C   That she is always dreaming

   D   That she is the daughter of a captain

3. Which of the following best describes the journey that Sara and her father have made?

   A   They have travelled from London to Bombay.

   B   They have travelled from London to India.

   C   They have travelled from India to London.

   D   They have travelled to Bombay from India.

4. According to the text, which of the following statements must be false?

   A   Sara has been to India.

   B   Sara's father captained the ship they travelled on.

   C   Sara is petite.

   D   Sara was the only female aboard the ship.

5. Which of the following reasons best explains Sara's actions in line 22?

    A   She moves closer to her father for comfort.

    B   She moves closer to her father because she is excited.

    C   She moves closer to her father for warmth.

    D   She moves closer to her father so that she can fall asleep on him.

6. What does "blazed" (line 2) mean?

    A   Flashed

    B   Glowed

    C   Flickered

    D   Reflected

7. What does "voyage" (line 14) mean?

    A   Movement

    B   Experience

    C   Challenge

    D   Journey

In each question below, the words can be rearranged to form a sentence. One word doesn't fit in the sentence. Underline the word that doesn't fit.

Example: bus   the   <u>caught</u>   waited   the   boy   for

---

8. the   smashed   apron   the   glasses   waitress

9. novel   Louise   to   fantasy   unicorns   decided   write   a

10. I   enjoy   put   cheesecake   like   raspberries   my   on   to

11. surfing   in   went   the   last   I   summer   ocean   dive

12. hooked   catch   fish   didn't   any   liked   fishing   he   but   Lee

13. started   jumper   my   holes   to   clothes   in   get   it   has

14. in   I   letter   my   Germany   friend   a   to   posts   sent   yesterday

Find the word that means the opposite, or nearly the opposite, of the word on the left.

Example: **love**   like   annoy   <u>hate</u>   enemy

15. **stop**   wait   continue   pause   movement

16. **follow**   instructor   lead   chase   guard

17. **reward**   harm   punish   praise   ignore

18. **timid**   excited   boring   confident   shy

19. **unusual**   random   proper   typical   strange

20. **professional**   amateur   expert   employee   useless

END OF TEST

/ 20

Test 2

You have **10 minutes** to do this test. Work as quickly and accurately as you can.

Fill in the missing letters to complete the words in the following passage.

1. Glass is a very ☐ s ☐ f ☐ l material, and many

2. o ☐ ☐ e c ☐ s that we use on a daily basis, such as windows,

3. light bulbs and pairs of ☐ p e ☐ ☐ a c ☐ e s are made from glass.

4. Today, glass is mainly ☐ r ☐ d ☐ c e ☐ in factories, but prior to this,

5. items made from glass were created by ☐ ☐ ☐ d , often using a technique

6. ☐ ☐ ☐ l l ☐ ☐ glassblowing. Glassblowing involves blowing air into

7. molten glass whilst forming the glass into ☐ i ☐ f ☐ r e ☐ t shapes.

8. It is an incredibly t ☐ i ☐ k ☐ skill to master, and glassblowing

9. apprentices would have spent years ☐ e a ☐ n ☐ n ☐ their craft.

10. On the Italian islands of Murano, t r ☐ d i ☐ i ☐ n ☐ l

11. glassmaking lives on, and t ☐ ☐ ☐ i s ☐ s flock to the area to watch

12. demonstrations and to ☐ ☐ r ☐ h ☐ s e souvenirs.

Complete the word on the right so that it means the opposite, or nearly the opposite, of the word on the left.

Example: start [e][n][d]

13. rarely [ ][f][ ][ ][n]

14. scowl [g][ ][ ][ ][n]

15. unlucky [b][l][ ][s][ ][ ][d]

16. single [ ][u][l][ ][ ][p][ ][e]

17. pleased [m][i][s][ ][r][ ][b][ ][e]

Three of the words in each list are linked.
Mark the word that is not related to these three.

Example: red   green   ~~stripy~~   blue

18. car   drive   van   lorry

19. sister   grandmother   niece   uncle

20. play   character   book   film

21. apple   lemon   lime   orange

22. burger   steak   meat   sausage

7

In each question below, the words can be rearranged to form a sentence. One word doesn't fit in the sentence. Underline the word that doesn't fit.

Example: bus the <u>caught</u> waited the boy for

23. loved classic watching movie Jennifer films Hollywood

24. my rumbled food hungry was because stomach I

25. the unprepared old fell weather for man the was

26. morning slept and in schedule this I behind was tired

END OF TEST

/ 26

You have **10 minutes** to do this test. Work as quickly and accurately as you can.

Choose the correct words to complete the passage below.

There are eighteen
1. □ same
□ different
□ new
□ whole
species of penguin around the world.

Nearly
2. □ any
□ every
□ each
□ all
penguins can be found south of the Equator, and they

3. □ settle
□ occupy
□ reside
□ habitat
each of the southern continents. Penguins are

4. □ part
□ portion
□ share
□ segment
of a

small group of birds that are unable to fly, but they are
5. □ well
□ much
□ far
□ total
adapted to life

in the water. Their streamlined bodies and flipper-like wings
6. □ produce
□ form
□ make
□ prepare
them

excellent swimmers, and their black and white feathers
7. □ support
□ guide
□ help
□ provide
effective

camouflage above and below the surface of the water.

8. Penguins
□ live
□ locate
□ attend
□ show
mostly on the coastline, feeding on a

9.
□ array
□ brand
□ variety
□ order

10. of marine life and
□ spending
□ consuming
□ devoting
□ putting
roughly 50-75% of their lives in water.

11. Despite this, penguins
□ unable
□ cannot
□ manage
□ can
breathe underwater, and therefore have to

12.
□ appear
□ enter
□ leave
□ come
up for air regularly.

Complete the word on the right so that it means the same, or nearly the same, as the word on the left.

Example: kind [c][a][r][i][n][g]

13. rich [w][ ][ ][l][t][ ][y]

14. find [d][ ][s][ ][o][ ][ ][r]

15. perfect [f][l][ ][w][e][ ][s]

16. regular [ ][r][ ][q][ ][e][n][t]

Mark the word outside the brackets that has a similar meaning to the words in both sets of brackets.

Example: (circle ring) (session game)   set   <u>round</u>   oval

17. (bead droplet)   (rip split)   fray   drip   tear

18. (force strength)   (can could)   might   power   may

19. (report document)   (smooth polish)   rub   file   folder

20. (live inhabit)   (worry brood)   ponder   dwell   reside

21. (delay stop)   (stand booth)   hinder   shop   stall

Three of the words in each list are linked.
Mark the word that is not related to these three.

Example: red   green   <u>stripy</u>   blue

22. stream   river   lake   puddle

23. spider   hornet   bee   wasp

24. beautiful   friendly   gorgeous   pretty

25. sneeze   cough   shout   snore

26. always   forever   eternally   temporarily

END OF TEST

/ 26

Puzzles 1

Time for a break! These puzzles are a great way to practise your **vocabulary** skills.

Synonym Finder

Complete the crossword by choosing an appropriate **synonym** for each word below.

ACROSS

1. foolish
2. tripped
3. study
4. gloomy
5. hobby
6. penniless

DOWN

1. taken
2. scent
3. weather
4. self-important
5. sea
6. fear

Odd One Out

Circle the odd one out in each of the lists below.
Add the wrong words to the box to complete the joke.

1. paint   easel   picture   ink   brush
2. thieve   steal   rob   burgle   jail
3. although   because   whereas   however   yet
4. framed   hidden   obscured   covered   secreted

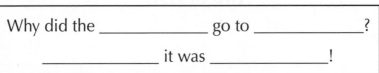

Why did the _____ go to _____?
_____ it was _____!

© CGP — not to be photocopied

12

Puzzles 1

You have **10 minutes** to do this test. Work as quickly and accurately as you can.

Read this passage carefully and answer the questions that follow.

An extract from 'Phantasmagoria'

One winter night, at half-past nine,
Cold, tired, and cross, and muddy,
I had come home, too late to dine,
And supper, with cigars and wine,
5   Was waiting in the study.

There was a strangeness in the room,
And Something white and wavy
Was standing near me in the gloom —
I took it for the carpet-broom
10   Left by that careless slavey*.

But presently the Thing began
To shiver and to sneeze:
On which I said "Come, come, my man!
That's a most inconsiderate plan.
15   Less noise there, if you please!"

"I've caught a cold," the Thing replies,
"Out there upon the landing."
I turned to look in some surprise,
And there, before my very eyes,
20   A little Ghost was standing!

He trembled when he caught my eye,
And got behind a chair.
"How came you here," I said, "and why?
I never saw a thing so shy.
25   Come out! Don't shiver there!"

He said "I'd gladly tell you how,
And also tell you why;
But" (here he gave a little bow)
"You're in so bad a temper now,
30   You'd think it all a lie.

"And as to being in a fright,
Allow me to remark
That Ghosts have just as good a right
In every way, to fear the light,
35   As Men to fear the dark."

Lewis Carroll

* slavey — *housemaid*

Answer these questions about the text that you've just read.
Circle the letter that matches the correct answer.

1. Which of the following is not mentioned in the text?

    A   What time of year it is

    B   What time of day it is

    C   Where the ghost caught a cold

    D   What made the narrator tired and cross

2. What causes the narrator to realise there is a ghost in the room?

    A   The narrator sees a white object.

    B   The narrator feels something strange.

    C   The narrator turns to face the ghost when the ghost talks to him.

    D   The ghost sneezes.

3. Why does the ghost hide behind the chair?

    A   He does not want to be noticed by the narrator.

    B   He is afraid of the narrator.

    C   He feels embarrassed.

    D   He is feeling unwell.

4. In line 30, why does the ghost think that the narrator will not believe him?

    A   Because the ghost's tale is not very plausible

    B   Because the ghost is not telling the truth

    C   Because the narrator does not believe in ghosts

    D   Because the narrator is annoyed

5. Which of the following adjectives best describes the ghost?

   A   Frightening

   B   Reckless

   C   Timid

   D   Sorrowful

6. What does "gloom" (line 8) mean?

   A   Corner

   B   Light

   C   Darkness

   D   Mist

7. What does "inconsiderate" (line 14) mean?

   A   Thoughtless

   B   Rowdy

   C   Ridiculous

   D   Irritating

Mark the word outside the brackets that has a similar meaning to the words in both sets of brackets.

Example: (circle ring) (session game)   set   <u>round</u>   oval

8. (goes exits)   (foliage vegetation)   plants   departs   leaves

9. (write jot)   (memo notice)   note   message   scrawl

10. (dish saucer)   (pitch throw)   hurl   bowl   plate

11. (blunt unsharpened) (boring uninteresting)   dull   flat   dry

12. (ray   shaft)   (smile   grin)   laugh   beam   light

13. (stool   seat)   (host   lead)   chair   present   sofa

14. (glass   reflector) (copy   mimic)   window   echo   mirror

---

Complete the word on the right so that it means the opposite,
or nearly the opposite, of the word on the left.

Example: start   [e][n][d]

---

15. strong   [f][ ][ ][i][l]

16. crouch   [ ][t][ ][e][ ][c][h]

17. gusty   [s][ ][ ][l][ ]

18. disappoint   [ ][m][p][ ][e][s][ ]

19. shabby   [s][m][ ][ ][ ]

20. help   [p][ ][ ][v][e][ ][t]

END OF TEST

/ 20

You have **10 minutes** to do this test. Work as quickly and accurately as you can.

> Fill in the missing letters to complete the words in the following passage.

1. Diwali, also called the festival of lights, is c ⬜ l e b ⬜ a t e ⬜

2. by Hindus around the world. It is normally h ⬜ ⬜ d in October or

3. November ⬜ ⬜ c h year, and it often lasts for five days.

4. Most Hindus observe Diwali in s ⬜ ⬜ i l ⬜ r ways.

5. Families p ⬜ e ⬜ ⬜ r e for the celebrations by cleaning and

6. d ⬜ c ⬜ r a ⬜ ⬜ n g their homes. On the main day of the

7. festival, people wear new c ⬜ ⬜ t h ⬜ s, participate in prayers

8. and light s m ⬜ l ⬜ lamps called 'diyas' in their homes and gardens.

9. They hope that these lamps will e n ⬜ o u ⬜ g e Lakshmi, the

10. goddess of wealth and good fortune, to enter ⬜ h e ⬜ ⬜ homes.

11. Later in the evening, people watch firework d ⬜ ⬜ p l ⬜ y s, take

12. part in family meals and ⬜ x c ⬜ a n ⬜ e gifts.

Find the word that means the same, or nearly the same, as the word on the left.

Example: **tub**   flask   <u>pot</u>   bottle   glass

13. **spoon**   dish   fork   ladle   slurp

14. **warning**   advise   tell   hint   caution

15. **glittering**   valuable   sparkling   polish   glossy

16. **rude**   impolite   angry   immature   annoying

17. **smell**   snort   sneeze   grunt   sniff

Complete the word on the right so that it means the opposite, or nearly the opposite, of the word on the left.

Example: start   ⌈e⌉⌈n⌉⌈d⌉

18. front   ☐ e a ☐

19. constant   i r ☐ ☐ g u ☐ ☐ r

20. cover   r ☐ v ☐ a l

21. thicken   d i l ☐ ☐ e

22. dry   s ☐ d ☐ ☐ n

Mark the word outside the brackets that has a similar meaning to the words in both sets of brackets.

Example: (circle ring) (session game)   set <u>round</u> oval

23. (cat dog)   (pat rub)   stroke   animal   pet

24. (dessert main)   (direction route) dish   course   path

25. (aim goal)   (spike end)   indicate   tip   point

26. (overweight plump) (lard butter)   fat   obese   oil

END OF TEST

/ 26

You have **10 minutes** to do this test. Work as quickly and accurately as you can.

Read this passage carefully and answer the questions that follow.

My Brother the Bear

James's mind had clouded over with a thick, dense fog of boredom. Show and tell was supposed to be engaging, but James had zoned out after the fifth (or was it the sixth?) action figure had been paraded around the classroom. James gazed out of the window as José demonstrated his figure's retractable armour and poseable limbs.
5   James heard what José was saying, but his mind failed to piece it together coherently. The sounds were just noise, drifting in one ear and straight out the other.
"Next, we have Carlos and his brother, Bernard," said Mrs. Davies. As Carlos went to invite Bernard into the classroom, a growl erupted from the other side of the door. James's mind snapped back into focus, perplexed by the bellowing noise. As
10   his eyes moved towards the door, James caught sight of a bear cub lumbering into the classroom.
"This is my brother, Bernard," Carlos said with a smile.
Now — and I must apologise for stating the obvious — this was a most unusual sight to behold, not simply because of the presence of the bear, or because he was
15   introduced as Carlos's brother, but also because he was dressed in a tatty green suit.
Carlos explained that, even though it was unconventional, Bernard was one of the family. Bernard slept on Carlos's bottom bunk, but he'd soon be too big, so Carlos's dad was making him a purpose-built bed. Although Bernard was usually well-behaved, he had a tendency to scratch the sofa, and the neighbours had
20   complained that he often scared their cat.
Carlos described how Bernard was a very loving brother, who could cheer him up without fail. Bernard even demonstrated some of his skills, such as his ability to wave and burp on cue. As Bernard's burp filled the classroom, the entire room swelled with laughter, and even James couldn't suppress a chuckle.

Answer these questions about the text that you've just read.
Circle the letter that matches the correct answer.

1. Which adjective best describes how James is feeling in lines 1-3?

    A   Annoyed

    B   Discouraged

    C   Tired

    D   Uninterested

2. José's voice is described as "drifting in one ear and straight out the other" (line 6).
   This means:

    A   James has poor hearing.

    B   James does not like the sound of José's voice.

    C   James is not paying attention.

    D   José is speaking too quietly.

3. Which of the following first gets James's attention?

    A   Mrs. Davies introducing Bernard.

    B   ~~The noise that Bernard makes.~~

    C   Bernard entering the classroom.

    D   The suit that Bernard is wearing.

4. Bernard is described as being "one of the family" (lines 16-17). This means:

    A   he resembles one of Carlos's relatives.

    B   he is related to Carlos.

    C   he is treated like a member of Carlos's family.

    D   he likes being a part of Carlos's family.

5. Which of the following statements must be false?

    A   Carlos's neighbour's cat is frightened of Bernard.

    B   Bernard is too big for Carlos's bunk bed.

    C   José owns an action figure.

    D   James finds Bernard amusing.

6. What does "tatty" (line 15) mean?

    A   Small

    B   Shabby

    C   Unusual

    D   Stylish

7. What does "lumbering" (line 10) mean?

    A   Walking carefully

    B   Walking clumsily

    C   Walking rapidly

    D   Walking noisily

Find the word that means the same, or nearly the same, as the word on the left.

        Example: **tub**   flask   <u>pot</u>   bottle   glass

---

8. **rigid**   stiff   bendy   strong   brittle

9. **aid**   fix   encourage   help   depend

10. **slow**   tired   sluggish   quiet   drowsy

11. **path**   highway   street   road   track

12. **walk**   stretch   stroll   race   gallop

13. **fill**   load   close   pour   tip

Mark the word outside the brackets that has a similar meaning to the words in both sets of brackets.

Example: (circle ring)   (session game)   set   <u>round</u>   oval

14. (annoy bother)   (flea mite)   bug   insect   pester

15. (arrow projectile) (dash hurtle)   bullet   dart   sprint

16. (notebook jotter)   (sneak creep)   trudge   book   pad

17. (rest pause)   (crack shatter)   stop   damage   break

18. (cereal corn)   (particle speck)   wheat   grain   fleck

19. (performers actors) (throw fling)   cast   hurl   parts

20. (total complete)   (speak say)   express   utter   full

END OF TEST

/ 20

These puzzles are bound to give your brain a workout.

Secret Treasure

Each blue tile contains the start of a word. Each white tile contains the end of a word. Match each blue tile with a white tile to make eight different words. Each tile can only be used once. Rearrange the words to reveal a hidden message about a stash of pirate treasure. The first word has been done for you.

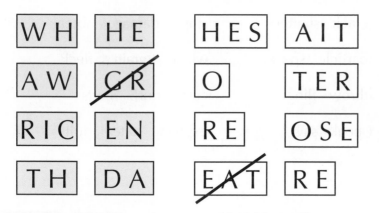

Use this space to jot down the words you can make.

Sentence: GREAT _____

_____.

Find the Letters

Work out the letter that each sentence refers to.
Rearrange the letters to find the chef's missing ingredient.

a. You'll find me twice in both **colonel** and **illiterate**: _____.

b. I'm a vowel in **renovate** but I'm not in **relegate**: _____.

c. I appear twice in **effect** and once in **influence**: _____.

d. I'm the most common consonant in **reproduce**: _____.

e. I'm the only vowel not present in **aerobic**: _____.

Ingredient:

_ _ _ _ _

CGP

11+

Verbal Reasoning
& Comprehension

Ages 9-10

The 10-Minute Tests Answer Book

Verbal Reasoning

For the CEM (Durham University) test

Practise • Prepare • Pass

Everything your child needs for 11+ success

Test 1 — pages 2-5

1. C
The setting is described as a "dark winter's day" (line 1). Line 1 also states that "the yellow fog hung so thick and heavy", showing that the weather is foggy. Line 10 states that Sara is "only seven" years old. The name of Sara's mother is not mentioned in the text.

2. B
In lines 6-7 Sara is described as having "a queer old-fashioned thoughtfulness in her big eyes". Lines 8-9 state that "one did not expect to see such a look on her small face", suggesting that it is the serious look in her eyes that is surprising about her.

3. C
Line 2 states that Sara and her father are now in London, and in line 20, Sara remembers travelling from India.

4. D
In line 20, Sara remembers being in India. The text does not mention whether Sara's father captained the ship they travelled on. In line 8, Sara is described as a "such a little girl", suggesting that she is petite — 'petite' means 'small'. Line 17 describes the "young officers' wives" who were also on the ship from Bombay. This means that Sara couldn't have been the only female aboard the ship.

5. A
In line 22, Sara finds the sudden change in her environment "puzzling", and in line 19 she thinks it is "queer". 'Queer' means 'strange'. These words suggest that she moves closer to her father for comfort, because the experience has been strange and confusing.

6. B
'blazed' means 'glowed'.

7. D
'voyage' means 'journey'.

8. apron
The words can be rearranged into the sentence 'The waitress smashed the glasses.'

9. unicorns
The words can be rearranged into the sentence 'Louise decided to write a fantasy novel.'

10. enjoy
The words can be rearranged into the sentence 'I like to put raspberries on my cheesecake.'

11. dive
The words can be rearranged into the sentence 'I went surfing in the ocean last summer.'

12. hooked
The words can be rearranged into the sentence 'Lee liked fishing but he didn't catch any fish.'

13. clothes
The words can be rearranged into the sentence 'My jumper has started to get holes in it.'

14. posts
The words can be rearranged into the sentence 'I sent a letter to my friend in Germany yesterday.'

15. continue
'stop' means 'to stay still', whereas 'continue' means 'to move forward'.

16. lead
'follow' means 'to continue after someone', whereas 'lead' means 'to show the way for others'.

17. punish
'reward' means 'to give someone something for doing well', whereas 'punish' means 'to discipline someone for doing badly'.

18. confident
'timid' means 'shy', whereas 'confident' means 'outgoing'.

19. typical
'unusual' means 'not normal' whereas 'typical' means 'normal'.

20. amateur
'professional' means 'someone who does something as a job', whereas 'amateur' means 'someone who does something as a hobby'.

Test 2 — pages 6-8

1. useful — 'Glass is a very useful material'

2. objects — 'many objects that we use'

3. spectacles — 'and pairs of spectacles'

4. produced — 'glass is mainly produced in factories'

5. hand — 'created by hand, often using a technique'

6. called — 'using a technique called glassblowing'

7. different — 'into different shapes.'

8. tricky — 'an incredibly tricky skill to master'

9. learning — 'spent years learning their craft.'

10. traditional — 'traditional glassmaking lives on'

11. tourists — 'tourists flock to the area'

12. purchase — 'to purchase souvenirs.'

13. often
'rarely' means 'infrequently', whereas 'often' means 'frequently'.

14. grin
'scowl' means 'an angry expression', whereas 'grin' means 'a happy expression'.

15. blessed
'unlucky' means 'not lucky', whereas 'blessed' means 'lucky'.

16. multiple
'single' means 'one', whereas 'multiple' means 'several'.

17. miserable
'pleased' means 'happy', whereas 'miserable' means 'unhappy'.

18. drive
The other three are types of vehicle.

19. uncle
The other three are female family members.

20. character
The other three are ways to tell stories.

21. apple
The other three are all citrus fruits.

22. meat
The other three are all ways of serving meat.

23. movie
The words can be rearranged into the sentence 'Jennifer loved watching classic Hollywood films.'

24. food
The words can be rearranged into the sentence 'My stomach rumbled because I was hungry.'

25. fell
The words can be rearranged into the sentence 'The old man was unprepared for the weather.'

26. tired
The words can be rearranged into the sentence 'I slept in this morning and was behind schedule.'

Test 3 — pages 9-11

1. different — 'eighteen **different** species of penguin'

2. all — 'Nearly **all** penguins can be found'

3. occupy — 'and they **occupy** each'

4. part — '**part** of a small group of birds'

5. well — 'they are **well** adapted'

6. make — '**make** them excellent swimmers'

7. provide — '**provide** effective camouflage'

8. live — 'Penguins **live** mostly on the coastline'

9. variety — 'feeding on a **variety** of marine life'

10. spending — 'and **spending** roughly 50-75%'

11. cannot — 'penguins **cannot** breathe underwater'

12. come — 'have to **come** up for air regularly.'

13. wealthy
Both words mean 'well off'.

14. discover
Both words mean 'to come upon something'.

15. flawless
Both words mean 'without defect'.

16. frequent
Both words mean 'occurring often'.

17. tear
'tear' can mean 'a drop of liquid from your eye' or 'to pull apart'.

18. might
'might' can mean 'power' or it can indicate the possibility of doing something.

19. file
'file' can mean 'a group of papers' or 'to rub something until it is smooth'.

20. dwell
'dwell' can mean 'to reside somewhere' or 'to think about something for a while'.

21. stall
'stall' can mean 'to hold something up' or 'a stand from which to sell things'.

22. puddle
The other three are all permanent bodies of water.

23. spider
The other three are all flying insects.

24. friendly
The other three mean 'attractive'.

25. shout
The other three are sounds you make unintentionally.

26. temporarily
The other three mean 'endlessly'.

Puzzles 1 — page 12

Synonym Finder

Odd One Out

1. picture
The other four are all things you use to make a picture.

2. jail
The other four mean 'taking something without permission'.

3. because
The other four are all used to introduce a different point of view.

4. framed
The other four all mean 'kept out of sight'.

The joke is '**Why did the picture go to jail? Because it was framed!**'

Test 4 — pages 13-16

1. D
Line 1 states that the poem takes place "One winter night, at half-past nine". Line 17 states that the ghost caught a cold "upon the landing". However, the text does not give the reason why the narrator is tired and cross.

2. C
Although the narrator feels a "strangeness" (line 6) and notices "Something white and wavy" (line 7), the narrator thinks it is a "carpet-broom" (line 9), not a ghost. Even when the ghost sneezes in line 12, the narrator doesn't realise it's a ghost until lines 18-20, when the narrator turns to face who is talking to him.

3. B
Lines 21-22 state that the ghost "trembled" and hid behind the chair when he was spotted by the narrator, suggesting that he is afraid of him.

3

4. D
In lines 29-30 the ghost says "You're in so bad a temper now, / You'd think it all a lie", which suggests that the ghost thinks the narrator won't believe him because he's annoyed.

5. C
The ghost is frightened of the narrator — in lines 21-22 he "trembled" and hid when he caught the narrator's eye. He also says that he is "in a fright" (line 31), and suggests that he "fear[s] the light" (line 34). This suggests that the ghost is timid.

6. C
'gloom' means 'darkness'.

7. A
'inconsiderate' means 'thoughtless'.

8. leaves
'leaves' can mean 'departs from somewhere' or 'the greenery of trees or plants'.

9. note
'note' can mean 'to write something down' or 'a message'.

10. bowl
'bowl' can mean 'a vessel for holding food' or 'to throw something through the air or along the ground'.

11. dull
'dull' can mean 'not sharp' or 'lacking interest or excitement'.

12. beam
'beam' can mean 'a ray of light' or 'to smile broadly'.

13. chair
'chair' can mean 'a piece of furniture used to sit on' or 'to be in charge of a meeting'.

14. mirror
'mirror' can mean 'a reflective surface' or 'to imitate'.

15. frail
'strong' means 'sturdy', whereas 'frail' means 'fragile'.

16. stretch
'crouch' means 'to bend down', whereas 'stretch' means 'to lengthen'.

17. still
'gusty' means 'windy', whereas 'still' means 'calm'.

18. impress
'disappoint' means 'to let down', whereas 'impress' means 'to make someone feel admiration'.

19. smart
'shabby' means 'scruffy', whereas 'smart' means 'neat'.

20. prevent
'help' means 'to assist', whereas 'prevent' means 'to block'.

Test 5 — pages 17-19

1. celebrated — 'is **celebrated** by Hindus'

2. held — 'normally **held** in'

3. each — 'October or November **each** year'

4. similar — 'observe Diwali in **similar** ways'

5. prepare — 'Families **prepare** for the celebrations'

6. decorating — '**decorating** their homes'

7. clothes — 'people wear new **clothes**'

8. small — 'light **small** lamps called 'diyas''

9. encourage — 'lamps will **encourage** Lakshmi'

10. their — 'to enter **their** homes'

11. displays — 'people watch firework **displays**'

12. exchange — 'and **exchange** gifts.'

13. ladle
Both words mean 'an implement for scooping food'.

14. caution
Both words mean a notice about a possible danger.

15. sparkling
Both words mean 'shimmering'.

16. impolite
Both words mean 'bad-mannered'.

17. sniff
Both words mean 'to inhale using the nose'.

18. rear
'front' means 'the foremost part of something', whereas 'rear' means 'the back of something'.

19. irregular
'constant' means 'continuously', whereas 'irregular' means 'intermittently'.

20. reveal
'cover' means 'to hide', whereas 'reveal' means 'to show'.

21. dilute
'thicken' means 'to make thicker', whereas 'dilute' means 'to water down'.

22. sodden
'dry' means 'not wet', whereas 'sodden' means 'very wet'.

23. pet
'pet' can mean 'an animal kept in the home' or 'to stroke affectionately'.

24. course
'course' can mean 'part of a meal' or 'a path on which to travel'.

25. point
'point' can mean 'an objective' or 'a sharp end'.

26. fat
'fat' can mean 'heavier than average' or a greasy product used in cooking.

Test 6 — pages 20-23

1. D
Lines 1-2 state that James's mind was full of a "dense fog of boredom", and that he had "zoned out". This suggests that James is uninterested.

2. C
Line 5 states that "James heard what José was saying, but his mind failed to piece it together coherently". This suggests that he wasn't paying attention to what he was listening to.

3. B
Line 9 states that "James's mind snapped back into focus" after he heard Bernard's growl in line 8.

4. C
The phrase 'one of the family' means 'to treat someone unrelated to you like a family member'.

5. B
Lines 19-20 state that "the neighbours had complained that he often scared their cat". José is showing his action figure in line 3. Line 24 states that James "couldn't suppress a chuckle" at Bernard. Lines 17-18 state that Bernard will "soon be too big" for the bunk bed, but he hasn't grown out of it yet.

6. B
'tatty' means 'shabby'.

7. B
'lumbering' means 'walking clumsily'.

8. stiff
Both words mean 'unbending'.

9. help
Both words mean 'to assist'.

10. sluggish
Both words mean 'at a low speed'.

11. track
Both words mean 'a way or trail'.

12. stroll
Both words mean 'to amble'.

13. load
Both words mean 'to put something into a container until it has reached capacity'.

14. bug
'bug' can mean 'to irritate someone' or 'an insect'.

15. dart
'dart' can mean 'a small pointed object thrown through the air' or 'to move very quickly'.

16. pad
'pad' can mean 'a book of paper' or 'to move softly'.

17. break
'break' can mean 'to stop what you're doing momentarily' or 'to damage something'.

18. grain
'grain' can mean 'a cereal grown for food, such as wheat' or 'a tiny amount of something'.

19. cast
'cast' can mean 'the people who play characters in a performance' or 'to throw something through the air'.

20. utter
'utter' can mean 'absolute' or 'to talk'.

Puzzles 2 — page 24
Secret Treasure

The sentence is Great riches await those who dare enter here.

Find the Letters

a. L
There are two 'l's in 'colonel' and two in 'illiterate'.

b. O
The vowels 'e', 'o' and 'a' occur in 'renovate', but 'o' does not appear in 'relegate'.

c. F
There are two 'f's in 'effect' and one in 'influence'.

d. R
'R' appears twice in 'reproduce', whereas the consonants 'p', 'd' and 'c' only appear once.

e. U
The other four vowels, 'a', 'e', 'i' and 'o', all occur in 'aerobic'.

The ingredient is **flour**.

Test 7 — pages 25-27

1. one
'**one** of the most recognisable buildings'

2. complete
'to **complete** the 103-storey structure.'

3. allow
'designed to **allow** airships to dock'

4. ensure
'a way to **ensure** that the Empire State'

5. broadcast
'to **broadcast** TV and radio'

6. made
'**made** up of offices'

7. open
'two observation decks **open**'

8. public
'open to the **public**'

9. clear
'if the weather is **clear**'

10. take
'Most people **take** the lift'

11. annual
'there's an **annual** race'

12. starts
'which **starts** at the ground floor'

13. angry
The other three mean 'eerie'.

14. house
The other three are parts of a house.

15. pig
The other three are all baby animals.

16. mend
The other three mean 'to damage'.

17. factory
The other three are places where members of the public might visit.

18. strong
Both words mean 'mighty'.

19. surprise
Both words mean 'to shock'.

20. intelligent
Both words mean 'clever'.

21. educate
Both words mean 'to tutor'.

22. stuff
'stuff' can mean 'to cram' or 'items or belongings'.

23. drink
'drink' can mean 'a beverage' or 'to swallow a liquid'.

24. saw
'saw' can mean 'to cut into something' or 'noticed'.

25. ruler
'ruler' can mean 'a governor' or 'a straight measuring stick'.

26. stir
'stir' can mean 'to blend with a spoon' or 'to awaken'.

Test 8 — pages 28-31

1. C
Lines 6-7 state that "The Globe is synonymous with Shakespeare because many of his plays were first performed there". 'Synonymous' means 'closely associated'.

2. B
Line 8 states that The Globe was a "circular structure". Line 14 states that The Globe had a "thatched roof", and line 9 states that The Globe had "seating around the sides".

3. B
The original Globe was constructed in 1599, and it burnt down in 1613. Therefore, it had been running for 14 years before it was destroyed.

4. D
The Globe reopened in 1614, a year after the original Globe burnt down (line 16). It then "stood for 30 years" (line 18), so it must have been pulled down in 1644.

5. D
Line 12 states that "the poorer audience members stood in the yard", suggesting that poorer members of society could afford to see plays in 17th century London. The second Globe was pulled down to make room for housing, not Shakespeare's Globe. Line 2 states that "20 000 Londoners went to the theatre every week", but it doesn't say that 20 000 Londoners went to The Globe every week. Line 17 states that "Shakespeare may have performed at this theatre", showing that he must have been alive when the second Globe was constructed.

6. B
Line 24 states that Shakespeare's Globe can "only hold audiences of half what it once could". The original Globe could hold 3000 people (line 10). Therefore 1500 people can watch a performance in Shakespeare's Globe.

7. C
Lines 22-23 state that Shakespeare's Globe "was built using similar materials and used 16th-century construction techniques", suggesting that the same building materials were sourced and that modern construction techniques were not used. It is also "a very accurate representation of the original" (line 22), suggesting that it is the same size as the original Globe, rather than twice the size. However lines 24-25 state that the third Globe "has to adhere to strict modern safety regulations", which suggests that it is not an exact copy of the original.

8. jokes
The words can be rearranged into the sentence 'The comedian was not very amusing.'

9. bowl
The words can be rearranged into the sentence 'I eat cereal for breakfast every morning.'

10. squeal
The words can be rearranged into the sentence 'The pig rolled around in the mud.'

11. went
The words can be rearranged into the sentence 'I had a black Labrador named Dougal.'

12. money
The words can be rearranged into the sentence 'I found a penny on the floor once'.

13. amaze
The words can be rearranged into the sentence 'My friend taught himself how to do magic tricks.'

14. slurp
The words can be rearranged into the sentence 'I was so thirsty I drank out of the fountain.'

15. dry
'wet' means 'full of water', whereas 'dry' means 'not wet'.

16. free
'capture' means 'to catch', whereas 'free' means 'to release'.

17. sturdy
'fragile' means 'likely to break', whereas 'sturdy' means 'unlikely to break'.

18. generosity
'greed' means 'selfishness', whereas 'generosity' means 'unselfishness'.

19. calm
'alarm' means 'to startle', whereas 'calm' means 'to soothe'.

20. rapid
'gradual' means 'at a slow rate', whereas 'rapid' means 'at a quick rate'.

Test 9 — pages 32-34

1. held
'**held** over 1000 patents'

2. student
'As a **student**'

3. considered
'Edison was **considered** disruptive.'

4. spent
'He only **spent** a short time at school'

5. being
'before **being** home-schooled'

6. bright
'Edison was a **bright** child'

7. eventually
'and **eventually** opened his own'

8. research
'opened his own **research** facility.'

9. allowed
'which **allowed** people to record sound'

10. Whilst
'**Whilst** this innovation is remarkable'

11. associated
'most commonly **associated** with the light bulb'

12. helped
'which **helped** to make lighting safer'

13. few
The words can be rearranged into the sentence
'My neighbour recently adopted some kittens.'

14. habitat
The words can be rearranged into the sentence
'Most lemurs live on the island of Madagascar.'

15. calculator
The words can be rearranged into the sentence
'Lynette was not very good at maths.'

16. skids
The words can be rearranged into the sentence
'I slipped on the ice on my way home.'

17. windy
'windy' can mean 'twisting' or 'blowy'.

18. stalk
'stalk' can mean 'to track' or 'a part of a plant'.

19. coat
'coat' can mean 'a protective outer garment'
or 'to add a layer' (e.g. of paint).

20. torn
'torn' can mean 'pulled apart' or 'unable to decide'.

21. loot
'loot' can mean 'a hoard of goods' or 'to burgle'.

22. subtract
'add' means 'plus', whereas 'subtract' means 'minus'.

23. hurry
'dawdle' means 'to walk slowly', whereas
'hurry' means 'to walk quickly'.

24. boastful
'humble' means 'modest', whereas 'boastful' means 'arrogant'.

25. eager
'unwilling' means 'reluctant', whereas 'eager' means 'keen'.

26. deter
'encourage' means 'to persuade someone
to do something', whereas 'deter' means 'to
dissuade someone from doing something'.

Puzzles 3 — page 35
Word Ladder
a) **drain**
b) **crawl**
c) **brain**
d) **drawl**
e) **drawn**
The words should go (from the bottom of the ladder to
the top of the ladder): **crawl**, **drawl**, **drawn**, **drain**, **brain**

Forwards Backwards
a) **straw** (makes '**warts**' backwards)
b) **strap** (makes '**parts**' backwards)
c) **bulb** (makes '**blub**' backwards)
d) **peek** (makes '**keep**' backwards)

Test 10 — pages 36-38

1. drink — 'a very popular **drink** in Britain'

2. leaves — 'made from the dried, crushed **leaves**'

3. grows — 'which **grows** in countries'

4. climate — 'with a warm, humid **climate**.'

5. flavour — 'becomes infused with their **flavour**.'

6. explanation — 'one **explanation** comes from'

7. legend — 'comes from a Chinese **legend**.'

8. nearby — 'from a **nearby** shrub'

9. accidentally — '**accidentally** creating the first'

10. rituals — 'Some countries also have special **rituals**'

11. ceremonies — 'tea **ceremonies** involve particular'

12. rules — 'involve particular **rules**'

13. rocket
The other three are all natural objects found in space.

14. forest
The other three are all made of stone.

15. eraser
The other three can be used to make a mark.

16. exercising
The other three are types of exercise.

17. soggy
The other three mean 'slick'.

18. peaceful
Both words mean 'calm'.

19. spread
Both words mean 'to disperse'.

20. bustling
Both words mean 'full of activity'.

21. simple
Both words mean 'easy'.

22. consider
Both words mean 'to ponder'.

23. animals
The words can be rearranged into the sentence
'Oliver's mum was a veterinary nurse.'

24. minutes
The words can be rearranged into the sentence
'I missed my train to London yesterday'.

25. swam
The words can be rearranged into the sentence
'The children caused havoc in the ball pool.'

26. taste
The words can be rearranged into the sentence
'The waiter did not give me what I ordered.'

Test 11 — pages 39-42

1. D
Line 8 states that the other houses on the street were
"so new and so neat", suggesting that they are modern
and well-kept. The text does not mention their size.

2. A
Lines 3-4 state that "over every window was a distorted
face cut out in the beam". Line 18 also states that the
little boy "certainly liked the old house best". The date of the
year in which the house was built is carved on the great beam
(lines 2-3), but the text does not state which year this was.

3. B
Lines 11-12 state that "the projecting windows stand
so far out, that no one can see from our windows what
happens in that direction!" This shows that the windows
of the old house obstruct the view of the other houses.

4. C
Line 7 describes the hole in the spout of the house's
guttering. Lines 4-5 state that "one storey stood forward
a great way over the other", showing that the house had
at least two storeys. Lines 8 and 16 both describe the
other houses on the street as "new". Line 16 states that
there were houses "On the other side of the street", implying
that there is more than one row of houses on the street.

5. A
Lines 12-13 describe the house's steps as being "as
broad as those of a palace", and as "high as to a church
tower". This suggests that it has steps that are both
wide and high. The dragon's head spout, which is part of
the gutters, is "leaden" (line 5). However, line 13 states
that the railings of the house are "iron" rather than brass.

6. A
'decayed' means 'rotten'.

7. D
'distorted' means 'misshapen'.

8. middle
'edge' means 'the side of something',
whereas 'middle' means 'the centre'.

9. ailing
'healthy' means 'well', whereas 'ailing' means 'sick'.

10. saddened
'delighted' means 'happy', whereas
'saddened' means 'unhappy'.

11. surly
'polite' means 'courteous', whereas
'surly' means 'uncourteous'.

12. bland
'spicy' means 'flavoured with spices',
whereas 'bland' means 'flavourless'.

13. juicy
'dry' means 'without moisture', whereas
'juicy' means 'succulent'.

14. bloom
'wither' means 'to wilt', whereas 'bloom' means 'to flourish'.

15. metal
The other three are all types of precious metal.

16. cotton
The other three are things that animals' coats are made of.

17. writing
The other three mean a drawing.

18. friend
The other three are names of relatives.

19. result
The other three mean 'commencement'.

20. acceptance
The other three describe not being in captivity.

Puzzles 4 — page 43
Build the Pyramid

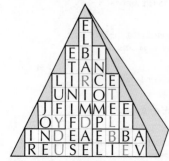

Hidden Words

1. Twins who look exactly alike are known as ide**ntica**l twins.
2. Aft**er m**uch trouble, Liu managed to close her window.
3. Joe had found a wa**y** to make himself invisible.
4. My uncle's hair**y ears** help him to hear better.
5. The train mu**st ar**rive on time or we will be late.

The synonym of happy is **merry**.

Test 12 — pages 44-46

1. pregnant — 'A **pregnant** frog will usually'

2. moist — 'in water or somewhere **moist**.'

3. form — 'These eggs **form** a clump'

4. surface — 'on the **surface** of the water'

5. number — 'lay a large **number** of eggs'

6. **survive** — 'only a few will **survive** into adulthood'

7. **substance** — 'protected by a jelly-like **substance**'

8. **diseases** — 'killed by predators or **diseases**.'

9. **hatch** — tadpoles will **hatch**'

10. **enable** — 'which **enable** them to swim easily'

11. **develop** — 'will **develop** lungs'

12. **fully** — 'and become a **fully** grown frog.'

13. **warm**
'warm' can mean 'heated' or 'welcoming'.

14. **dream**
'dream' can mean 'an ambition' or 'a vision when you sleep'.

15. **picture**
'picture' can mean 'a drawing' or 'to see something in the mind'.

16. **spare**
'spare' can mean 'to let go' or 'supplementary'.

17. **moor**
'moor' can mean 'an area of untended land ' or 'to secure' (e.g. a boat).

18. **play**
The words can be rearranged into the sentence 'The umpire said the ball was out.'

19. **brace**
The words can be rearranged into the sentence 'Martin had an appointment with the dentist.'

20. **pools**
The words can be rearranged into the sentence 'I have started swimming to improve my fitness.'

21. **exams**
The words can be rearranged into the sentence 'My friend was happy with her test results.'

22. **present**
The words can be rearranged into the sentence 'A jumper I received for Christmas is really itchy.'

23. **false**
'true' means 'accurate' whereas 'false' means 'inaccurate'.

24. **thaw**
'freeze' means 'to become icy' whereas 'thaw' means 'to melt'.

25. **prisoner**
'guard' means 'someone who is holding someone captive' whereas 'prisoner' means 'someone who is being held captive'.

26. **reckless**
'careful' means 'cautious' whereas 'reckless' means 'rash'.

Test 13 — pages 47-50

1. B
Line 3 states that the Amazon Rainforest is located in "an area of South America", not the United States. Line 3 also states that the Amazon Rainforest is located "in the Amazon River Basin", not the other way around. Lines 8-9 state that the Amazon Rainforest is home to "at least 10% of all the known species on our planet", rather than at least 10% of all life on Earth. Lines 12-13 state that "scientists believe many of the rainforest's species remain unknown and unclassified", showing that there are many more species in the Amazon Rainforest than we know about.

2. D
Lines 15-16 state that "mosquitoes carry diseases such as malaria". Lines 24-25 state that "Deforestation has also caused the destruction of animal habitats, and every day multiple species become extinct" which suggests that deforestation is causing the extinction of some animals. Line 6 mentions "the river that runs through the rainforest", however there is no mention of humans being unable to survive in the Amazon Rainforest.

3. D
There are over 400 species of mammals and 400 species of reptile (lines 10-11). However there are "24 000 species of trees, fish, birds and amphibians" (lines 11-12). It isn't clear how many of the 24 000 are trees, therefore it cannot be known from the text whether there are more trees than mammals and reptiles.

4. C
Lines 20-21 state that the Amazon Rainforest is called 'The Lungs of the Planet' because its "plant life produces about 20% of the world's oxygen while absorbing carbon dioxide from the atmosphere".

5. D
Line 2 states that the world's "largest tropical rainforest is the Amazon Rainforest". Lines 3-4 also state that the United States is twice the size of the Amazon Rainforest, which is itself over 20 times the size of the UK. Therefore the United States must be more than 20 times the size of the UK. The Amazon River is the second-longest river in the world and is over 6400 km (line 7). Therefore the longest river in the world must be over 6400 km. In the text, cattle farming is only said to be "partly" (line 23) responsible for the destruction of around 20% of the Amazon Rainforest.

6. B
'astounding' means 'amazing'.

7. A
'stabilise' means 'maintain'.

8. ate
The words can be rearranged into the sentence 'The baby tried to reach the plum.'

9. splash
The words can be rearranged into the sentence 'The alligator snapped his jaws in anger.'

10. them
The words can be rearranged into the sentence 'I accidentally spilt my drink on the floor.'

11. fast
The words can be rearranged into the sentence
'I asked for extra cheese on my burger.'

12. wind
The words can be rearranged into the sentence
'Cathy liked to go sailing on the lake.'

13. shade
The words can be rearranged into the sentence
'The girl read her book under the oak tree.'

14. dark
The words can be rearranged into the sentence
'Eric was scared when his bedroom light was turned off.'

15. damaged
Both words mean 'in need of repair'.

16. select
Both words mean 'to pick'.

17. hilarious
Both words mean 'amusing'.

18. noise
Both words mean 'something audible'.

19. perform
Both words mean 'to show'.

20. courageous
Both words mean 'fearless'.

Test 14 — pages 51-54

1. D
Line 1 states that the narrator comes from "a small, rural community", but it doesn't say where this is.

2. C
The phrase 'culture shock' means 'feeling disorientated by an unfamiliar environment'. The narrator finds London disorientating and unfamiliar.

3. C
In line 6 the narrator states that the Tube makes him feel uneasy because he is "quite claustrophobic". 'Claustrophobia' is a fear of confined places.

4. B
In lines 12-16 everyone else is using the ticket barriers quickly and easily, whereas the narrator "clumsily" inserts his ticket "while a queue of people formed behind me". This suggests that he feels flustered, because he is holding people up.

5. B
In lines 22-23 the narrator describes the Underground map as "a series of coloured lines snaking around one another in an unfathomable mess". 'Unfathomable' means 'difficult to understand'. This suggests that the map is very confusing for the narrator.

6. B
'vital' means 'necessary'.

7. B
'sedate' means 'calm'.

8. delicate
Both words mean 'soft'.

9. latch
Both words mean a fastening for something.

10. disappear
Both words mean 'to pass from sight'.

11. incline
Both words mean 'a slope'.

12. pause
Both words mean 'a break'.

13. explanation
Both words mean 'a justification'.

14. ask
Both words mean 'to appeal for something'.

15. guitar
The other three are all musical instruments you blow into.

16. table
The other three are all pieces of furniture you sit on.

17. water
The other three are all containers for liquids.

18. fence
The other three are types of plants.

19. medicine
The other three are medical professionals.

20. complicate
The other three all mean 'to explain'.

Puzzles 5 — page 55
Picture Words

POSTBOX, RAINBOW, TIMETABLE, UPDATE, CAREFREE, WATERTIGHT, STOPWATCH, AIRLINE, EARTHQUAKE

Test 15 — pages 56-58

1. period
'a **period** from about'

2. before
'and **before** the Romans invaded.'

3. lived
'usually **lived** in roundhouses'

4. villages
'in small **villages** or larger towns.'

5. was
'**was** quite complex.'

6. had
'**had** to be marked out.'

7. rested
'**rested** on wooden beams'

8. extended
'which **extended** into the centre'

9. Finally
'**Finally**, the walls were plastered'

10. made
'which was **made** of

10

11. helped
'Daub **helped** the house to retain heat'

12. protection
'some **protection** from the weather.'

13. go
The words can be rearranged into the sentence
'The weather outside was dark and stormy.'

14. restaurant
The words can be rearranged into the sentence
'The family went out for a delicious meal.'

15. kitchen
The words can be rearranged into the sentence
'Trevor liked baking but never followed the recipe.'

16. sight
The words can be rearranged into the sentence
'There are really stunning views in the countryside.'

17. floor
'ceiling' means 'the surface of a room above your head'
whereas 'floor' means 'the surface of a room under your feet'.

18. modest
'arrogant' means 'self-important',
whereas 'modest' means 'humble'.

19. slippery
'sticky' means 'likely to stick together',
whereas 'slippery' means 'likely to slide'.

20. crooked
'straight' means 'without bends',
whereas 'crooked' means 'bent'.

21. exclude
'involve' means 'to include', whereas 'exclude' means 'to omit'.

22. sink
The other three all mean 'to grow'.

23. shape
The other three are all types of shapes.

24. Germany
The other three are all languages.

25. chop
The other three mean 'to combine'.

26. tickle
The other three are sounds you might
make when being tickled.

Test 16 — pages 59-62

1. B
In lines 2-3 the narrator states "It would have
been nice to have lit it during the daylight", which
suggests that he wanted to light the campfire
earlier so they could do it before it became dark.

2. C
The text does not state what time of year the camping
trip takes place. The text doesn't mention whether
Jenna brought a torch with her. Line 10 states that the
group hovered around the fire "like moths", but the text
does not mention any actual moths being attracted
to the fire. However, lines 11-13 describe the group
cooking sausages and marshmallows on the campfire.

3. D
'Lulled' means 'became quiet' — therefore the
conversation stopped for a moment.

4. C
As well as the narrator, four other people are mentioned
in the text: Jenna, Marcus, Beth and Karim.

5. C
In lines 17-18 the narrator states "Personally, these
tales did nothing to make me feel uneasy, but I enjoyed
the atmosphere anyway". This suggests that the ghost
stories didn't make him feel scared, but he liked the mood
they created.

6. D
'artificial' means 'unnatural'

7. A
'eerie' means 'unsettling'.

8. post
'post' can mean 'a stick in the ground' or 'letters and parcels'.

9. duck
'duck' can mean a type of bird or 'to stoop down'.

10. well
'well' can mean 'a watering hole' or 'in good health'.

11. fine
'fine' can mean 'wispy' or 'acceptable'.

12. coast
'coast' can mean 'the edge of the land by the
sea' or 'to move without much effort'.

13. gloomy
'gloomy' can mean 'unhappy' or 'cloudy'.

14. spot
'spot' can mean 'to see something' or 'a mark on the skin'.

15. same
The words can be rearranged into the sentence
'Rose was reading several books at once.'

16. adores
The words can be rearranged into the sentence
'Lizzie has an incredibly strong love of pugs.'

17. frozen
The words can be rearranged into the sentence
'I wore my coat because it was chilly.'

18. audience
The words can be rearranged into the sentence
'Lauren's dream was to be in a play.'

19. ran
The words can be rearranged into the sentence
'Jeremy had to walk to school on his own.'

20. help
The words can be rearranged into the sentence
'The man showed us the way to the office.'

Puzzles 6 — page 63

Antonym Anagrams

a) Anagram **light**   Antonym **heavy**
b) Anagram **hungry**   Antonym **full**
c) Anagram **answer**   Antonym **question**
d) Anagram **freeze**   Antonym **melt**
e) Anagram **pleasure**   Antonym **sadness**

Shuffled Sentences

1. <u>Excited</u> was <u>everyone</u> to see the band at the concert.
2. After <u>the</u> discussion, we elected Sidra to be <u>some</u> leader for our team.
3. Having seen the <u>them</u> play, I thought I would congratulate <u>team</u>.
4. <u>Diana</u> as she turned the corner, <u>just</u> remembered to fetch her lunch.

The sentence is:
"1) **Everyone** screamed, and 2) **some** ran away, until I told 3) **them** that he 4) **just** wanted to play!"

Test 17 — pages 64-66

1. **born** — 'Galileo Galilei was **born** near Pisa'
2. **studied** — 'Although he **studied** philosophy'
3. **remembered** — 'he is mainly **remembered**'
4. **invention** — 'heard about the **invention** of the telescope'
5. **version** — 'He built a better **version**'
6. **Through** — '**Through** observation'
7. **believe** — 'he came to **believe**'
8. **people** — 'as most **people** thought'
9. **findings** — 'publicise his **findings**'
10. **banned** — 'he was **banned** from talking about them'
11. **arrest** — 'put under house **arrest**.'
12. **lifetime** — 'in his **lifetime**'
13. **month**
The other three are all times of the day.
14. **accept**
The other three all mean 'to argue against'.
15. **face**
The other three are all parts of the face.

16. **artist**
The other three are things that are used to make a painting.
17. **drought**
The other three are types of storms.
18. **silence**
Both words mean 'peace'.
19. **creepy**
Both words mean 'frightening'.
20. **yank**
Both words mean 'to tug'.
21. **faraway**
Both words mean 'not near'.
22. **well-behaved**
Both words describe someone who follows instructions.
23. **lean**
'lean' can mean 'to put at an angle' or 'slender'.
24. **jam**
'jam' can mean 'a fruity spread' or 'to pack in tightly'.
25. **feel**
'feel' can mean 'to touch something' or 'to believe'.
26. **hide**
'hide' can mean 'the coat of an animal' or 'to conceal'.

Test 18 — pages 67-70

1.   A
Lines 7-9 state that Nefertiti's bust has helped her to become regarded as one of "the most beautiful women of all time". The artworks described in lines 10-12 also show her defeating enemies, suggesting that she was powerful, and leading worship, suggesting that she was religious. However, the artworks do not show her as being mysterious.

2.   D
Lines 15-16 state that "some historians claim" Nefertiti was a Syrian princess, which suggests that this hasn't been proven. It is the sculpture of Nefertiti that is missing an eye, rather than Nefertiti herself. Line 15 states that Ay was a Pharaoh of Egypt, rather than Syria. Line 16 states that Nefertiti disappeared around "the twelfth year of Akhenaten's reign". A decade is ten years, so this means that Akhenaten must have reigned for more than a decade.

3.   D
Lines 13-16 give different theories about Nefertiti's early years, which suggests no-one knows for sure where she was born. The text does not give the name of the German archaeologist. Line 20 states that "Nefertiti's final resting place has yet to be identified", suggesting that her remains haven't been found. However, lines 4-5 state that Nefertiti's husband was Pharaoh Akhenaten.

4.   C
Line 17 states that Nefertiti's disappearance "remains a highly debated topic". This suggests that what happened to Nefertiti in later life is the most mysterious aspect of her life.

5.   **C**

Lines 8-9 state that some people have considered Nefertiti to be "one of the most beautiful women of all time", but this is only the opinion of some people, not everybody. Nefertiti's bust was discovered by a German archaeologist (line 6), but the text does not say that the bust was found in Germany. Lines 18-19 suggest that Nefertiti may have changed her name, but it is only a "theory". However the artworks of Nefertiti described in lines 10-11 show her alongside her children, meaning that she must have been a mother.

6.   **D**

'exceptional' means 'extraordinary'.

7.   **C**

'subsequent' means 'later'.

8.   **windy**

The other three mean 'cloudy'.

9.   **cook**

The other three are foodstuffs.

10.   **trim**

The other three mean 'to make longer'.

11.   **wicked**

The other three mean 'a scary creature'.

12.   **passenger**

The other three are job titles.

13.   **explosion**

The other three mean 'a sudden burst of light'.

14.   **lucky**

Both words mean 'blessed'.

15.   **trick**

Both words mean 'to fool someone'.

16.   **drench**

Both words mean 'to get very wet'.

17.   **occasion**

Both words mean 'an occurrence'.

18.   **squabble**

Both words mean 'to bicker'.

19.   **healthy**

Both words mean 'nourishing'.

20.   **disrupt**

Both words mean 'to interrupt'.

Test 19 — pages 71-73

1.   suggest — 'Some people might **suggest**'

2.   activity — 'a childish **activity**'

3.   steady — 'It takes a **steady** hand'

4.   elaborate — 'the results are often **elaborate** and impressive.'

5.   hours — 'It can take many **hours**'

6.   artist — 'so the **artist** will pick'

7.   incoming — 'from the **incoming** tide.'

8.   seaside — 'Several **seaside** towns'

9.   allow — 'which **allow** both'

10.   talents — 'to showcase their **talents**.'

11.   durable — 'as **durable** as possible'

12.   eventually — 'but **eventually** the sculptures'

13.   **ate**

The words can be rearranged into the sentence 'A butterfly landed on our picnic table.'

14.   **walks**

The words can be rearranged into the sentence 'My dad likes to stroll along the coast.'

15.   **talks**

The words can be rearranged into the sentence 'Melinda was not a fan of speaking in public.'

16.   **pain**

The words can be rearranged into the sentence 'My legs were sore after a long run.'

17.   **watch**

The words can be rearranged into the sentence 'I listened to my friend play in the concert.'

18.   **unsure**

Both words mean 'hesitant'.

19.   **complex**

Both words mean 'hard'.

20.   **essential**

Both words mean 'necessary'.

21.   **preserve**

Both words mean 'to retain'.

22.   **honest**

Both words mean 'sincere'.

23.   **sour**

'sweet' means 'sugary', whereas 'sour' means 'acidic'.

24.   **chaos**

'order' means 'control', whereas 'chaos' means 'out of control'.

25.   **conceal**

'reveal' means 'to show', whereas 'conceal' means 'to hide'.

26.   **trusting**

'suspicious' means 'wary', whereas 'trusting' means 'believing'.

Puzzles 7 — page 74

Multiple Machines

a) **tool, loot, foot, feet**
b) **fire, file, life, lives**
c) **sink, float, loaf, loaves**
d) **hose, house, mouse, mice**

Test 20 — pages 75-78

1.   **C**

The most likely reason that the sign is red is to get people's attention, because it is warning people not to touch the dinosaur. There is no evidence to support options A, B or D.

2. C

Line 4 states that the dinosaur is "lit up in cold white rays". The children walk around the dinosaur "in awe" (line 5), suggesting that they are impressed by it. Line 19 states "his owners turn a profit", suggesting that the owners make money from displaying the dinosaur. However, the guests are not encouraged to touch the dinosaur — there is a sign telling them not to (line 1).

3. A

Line 6 describes the dinosaur's "giant bones", suggesting that he was large. Lines 9-10 describe him as a 'hunter, / stalking puny, paltry prey", showing that he must have eaten meat.

4. B

Lines 25-26 state "One day will we be just the same: / brought out for a curious eye?". The narrator wonders whether, in the future, humans might be exhibited just like dinosaurs. In lines 27-28, the narrator asks "Will they describe us from our lives, / or from what our bones imply?". The narrator wonders whether human bones might one day be studied by researchers like dinosaur bones.

5. B

'Resolve' means 'conclusion', so "a riddle with no resolve" means a riddle without an answer.

6. A

'puny' means 'weak'.

7. B

'bygone' means 'former'.

8. elated

Both words mean 'extremely happy'.

9. stop

Both words mean 'to come to a standstill'.

10. stretch

Both words mean 'to extend'.

11. enormous

Both words mean 'huge'.

12. yearn

Both words mean 'to long for'.

13. empty

Both words mean 'unoccupied'.

14. clever

The other three mean 'faithful'.

15. neglect

The other three mean 'to watch over something'.

16. scream

The other three mean 'to chatter'.

17. island

The other three are places for mooring boats.

18. calendar

The other three show you the time of day.

19. relieved

The other three mean 'astonished'.

20. develop

The other three mean 'to end'.

Test 21 — pages 79-82

1. B

Lines 3-4 describe the "long, furry handles" of the bell-ropes, which look like "great caterpillars".

2. D

Lines 5-6 describe the bells as "very big and dusty", suggesting they haven't been cleaned for a long time. Line 13 states that "people have cut their names" on the top of the tower, and line 6 describes the "four windows" where the bells are kept. However in line 5, the narrator states that the children "did not pull" the bell-ropes, so they did not ring the bells.

3. B

In lines 7-9, the children aren't certain if the heaps of straws and sticks are owls' nests. Mrs Simpkins's cottage looks very small from the tower (line 16), but the text doesn't mention whether it is actually a small or large cottage. The bell-ropes are described as being either red or blue and white in line 4. However, lines 1-2 state that the door to the church tower "had always been locked before".

4. D

The farms seem very small from the top of the tower because they are far away. Therefore, they look like toy versions of farms.

5. A

Lines 17-18 describe the "corn-fields" as well as the grassy "meadows and pastures". Line 19 describes the "hedges". Although the wall in line 14 looks like "castle battlements", a castle cannot be seen from the tower.

6. D

'ajar' means 'open'.

7. C

'suddenly' means 'abruptly'.

8. purchase

The words can be rearranged into the sentence 'The school hosted a charity bake sale.'

9. time

The words can be rearranged into the sentence 'Johan always forgets to turn back the clocks.'

10. orange

The words can be rearranged into the sentence 'Kirsty always peels her apples before eating them.'

11. coin

The words can be rearranged into the sentence 'He had lost the money for the bus.'

12. eaten

The words can be rearranged into the sentence 'My mum cooked my favourite meal for dinner.'

13. mug

The words can be rearranged into the sentence 'Kristina prefers her tea with a splash of milk.'

14. present

The words can be rearranged into the sentence 'I bought a bauble to hang on my Christmas tree.'

15. cook

'cook' can mean 'to heat up food' or 'someone who makes meals'.

14

16. coach
'coach' can mean 'a large vehicle with lots of seats' or 'a mentor'.

17. film
'film' can mean 'a motion picture' or 'a thin layer on a surface'.

18. fan
'fan' can mean 'to move air' or 'a devotee'.

19. drain
'drain' can mean 'to make weary' or 'a pipe where wastewater flows'.

20. root
'root' can mean 'basis' or 'to forage'.

Test 22 — pages 83-85

1. particularly
'**particularly** the area of Andalucia.'

2. normally
'**normally** made up of three parts'

3. playing
'singing, dancing and guitar **playing**.'

4. lots
'with **lots** of arm movements'

5. expressions
'strong facial **expressions**.'

6. typically
'Women **typically** wear long dresses'

7. might
'men **might** wear black trousers'

8. play
'Dancers also **play** the castanets'

9. together
'two wooden shells that are clicked **together**.'

10. important
'an **important** part of Spanish culture'

11. celebrated
'it is **celebrated** with its own festival'

12. every
'**every** two years.'

13. before
'after' means 'following', whereas 'before' means 'prior'.

14. hinder
'help' means 'to assist', whereas 'hinder' means 'to block'.

15. extinguished
'lit' means 'set alight', whereas 'extinguished' means 'put out'.

16. recall
'forget' means 'to be unable to remember', whereas 'recall' means 'to remember'.

17. sack
'sack' can mean 'to remove someone from employment' or 'a container for someone's possessions'.

18. pen
'pen' can mean 'an enclosure for animals' or 'something to write with'.

19. bar
'bar' can mean 'to prohibit' or 'a rod'.

20. raw
'raw' can mean 'not cooked' or 'cold'.

21. strain
'strain' can mean 'to squeeze out water' or 'a lot of pressure'.

22. contest
Both words mean 'a tournament'.

23. trunk
Both words mean 'a box'.

24. jog
Both words mean 'to run at a leisurely pace'.

25. reject
Both words mean 'to deny'.

26. waste
Both words mean 'to throw away'.

Puzzles 8 — page 86

Canine Connections

Dad Rover: **effort**
Cousin Rover: **nervously**
Gran Rover: **exhaustion**
Mum Rover: **sporty**
Uncle Rover: **dove**

Word Wheel

create eternal later elegant
Nine letter word: **rectangle**

Test 23 — pages 87-89

1. home — '**home** to the ring-tailed lemur'

2. fur — 'with grey **fur**'

3. with — 'along **with** some tiny'

4. world — 'only place in the **world**'

5. wild — 'in the **wild**'

6. think — 'Some people **think**'

7. arrived — 'may have **arrived**'

8. ago — 'millions of years **ago**'

9. diet — 'The **diet** of the ring-tailed lemur'

10. species — 'Unlike other **species** of lemur'

11. amongst — '**amongst** the treetops'

12. foraging — '**foraging** for food on the ground.'

13. ambition
Both words mean 'an aim'.

14. nimble
Both words mean 'agile'.

15. chisel
Both words mean 'to cut into a surface'.

16. extend
Both words mean 'to lengthen'.

17. statement
Both words mean 'a formal message'.

18. valley
The other three are all high parts of land.

19. idle
The other three mean 'energetic'.

20. sleepy
The other three mean 'warm and comfortable'.

21. visitor
The other three mean 'an opponent'.

22. politician
The other three are people who look after your health.

23. fight
The words can be rearranged into the sentence
'My neighbour's cat really dislikes the dogs.'

24. pick
The words can be rearranged into the sentence
'John had forgotten to take his dinner money.'

25. travel
The words can be rearranged into the sentence
'Sandra always went on holiday in the spring.'

26. but
The words can be rearranged into the sentence
'They had to cross the river at the bridge.'

Test 24 — pages 90-92

1. compete
'where athletes **compete**'

2. highest
'jump the **highest**'

3. participant
'Each **participant** tries'

4. each
'after **each** round.'

5. competitors
'most **competitors** would clear'

6. famous
'One of the most **famous** high jumpers'

7. pioneered
'He **pioneered** a new technique'

8. involved
'which **involved** jumping over the bar backwards'

9. landing
'and **landing** on his back'

10. softer
'new, **softer** landing mats.'

11. technique
'the main **technique**'

12. current
'the **current** world record holder'

13. competed
The words can be rearranged into the sentence
'Bradley took part in a triathlon recently.'

14. so
The words can be rearranged into the sentence
'George and his sister collected stamps from America.'

15. blaze
The words can be rearranged into the sentence
'The log fire crackled and warmed the room.'

16. ate
The words can be rearranged into the sentence
'I am a messy eater when I eat spaghetti.'

17. cottage
The other three are places farm animals are kept.

18. koala
The other three are primates.

19. food
The other three mean 'appetising'.

20. surfboard
The other three are enclosed vehicles
that travel on the water.

21. decided
The other three mean 'considered'.

22. can
'can' can mean 'a metal food container'
or 'to possibly do something'.

23. live
'live' can mean 'to be alive' or 'to inhabit somewhere'.

24. view
'view' can mean 'a belief' or 'a scenic landscape'.

25. cool
'cool' can mean 'to make colder' or 'stylish'.

26. flat
'flat' can mean 'without bumps' or 'an apartment'.

Test 25 — pages 93-96

1. D
Lines 9-10 state that "Friends may be gone in the morning fair". This suggests that friends are unreliable because they might leave without warning, unlike the cliffs which are "always there".

2. C
"ward" means 'to guard'. This suggests that the cliffs protect the land.

3. B
In line 20, the narrator mentions "the wreck I'd saved had I kept to sea". This suggests that his ship sank.

4. D
Line 6 describes the "sandhill" (sand dune) and "sandy beach", and line 27 mentions a "field". The text doesn't mention a forest.

5. B
Line 14 states that the cliffs "warn the ships from the treacherous sand" and in line 18, "They point the ships to keep seaward still". This suggests that the cliffs alert the sailors to the land ahead.

6. B
'grandeur' means 'magnificence'.

7. D
'treacherous' means 'dangerous'.

8. finish
Both words mean 'to end'.

9. respect
Both words mean 'appreciation'.

10. motion
Both words mean 'action'.

11. fresh
Both words mean 'recent'.

12. pursue
Both words mean 'to track'.

13. genuine
Both words mean 'authentic'.

14. drop
'lift' means 'to raise up', whereas 'drop' means 'to let fall'.

15. worst
'best' means 'the most good', whereas 'worst' means 'the least good'.

16. handsome
'ugly' means 'unattractive', whereas 'handsome' means 'attractive'.

17. intricate
'simple' means 'not difficult', whereas 'intricate' means 'difficult'.

18. sorrowful
'glad' means 'happy', whereas 'sorrowful' means 'unhappy'.

19. deft
'clumsy' means 'awkward', whereas 'deft' means 'agile'.

20. combine
'separate' means 'to take apart', whereas 'combine' means 'to mix together'.

Puzzles 9 — page 97

Monster Rhymes

There are no right or wrong answers, but here are some suggestions.

First column: **dare**, **fright**, **scary**, **floor**

Second column: **bared**, **head**, **dream**

Accept any sensible conclusion to the poem. The last words of each of the final two lines (written by the child) should rhyme with each other.

Sound It Out

1. witch   which
2. blew   blue
3. piece   peace
4. ate   eight
5. rung   wrung

Test 26 — pages 98-100

1. fabric — 'delicate, shiny **fabric**'
2. luxurious — '**luxurious** clothes and furnishings'
3. practical — 'more **practical** uses'
4. Unlike — '**Unlike** some materials'
5. Instead — '**Instead**, it's made from'
6. that — '**that** spin cocoons'
7. threads — 'spun into silk **threads**.'
8. use — 'to **use** silk'
9. precious — 'became a **precious** item'
10. time — 'length of **time**.'
11. largest — '**largest** producer of silk'
12. approximately — 'for **approximately** one million'

13. staff
'staff' can mean 'a rod' or 'the people who work for a company'.

14. sunny
'sunny' can mean 'joyful' or 'a bright day'.

15. rich
'rich' can mean 'containing lots of butter or cream' or 'affluent'.

16. produce
'produce' can mean 'a harvest' or 'to make something'.

17. harmony
'harmony' can mean 'agreement of feeling' or 'a pleasing combination of musical notes'.

18. kitchen
The other three are places you can eat out.

19. soil
The other three mean 'to excavate'.

20. couple
The other three are groups of animals.

21. exciting
The other three mean 'unremarkable'.

22. marble
The other three are precious gems.

23. defend
Both words mean 'to guard'.

24. fall
Both words mean 'to trip over'.

25. demolish
Both words mean 'to break up completely'.

26. dirty
Both words mean 'not clean'.

Test 27 — pages 101-103

1. by
'played **by** blowing'

2. produce
'to **produce** different notes'

3. which
'on **which** the keys are found'

4. exit
'for the sound to **exit**.'

5. wanted
'who **wanted** to create an instrument'

6. combined
'that **combined** the quick notes'

7. of
'**of** a woodwind instrument'

8. along
'**along** with the metal body'

9. qualities
'merge these **qualities**.'

10. now
'they are **now** more commonly associated'

11. with
'more commonly associated **with** jazz music.'

12. talent
'demonstrate their **talent**.'

13. crunchy
'soft' means 'not crisp', whereas 'crunchy' means 'crisp'.

14. swell
'deflate' means 'to reduce in size', whereas 'swell' means 'to grow in size'.

15. trap
'release' means 'to let go', whereas 'trap' means 'to catch'.

16. hopeful
'disheartened' means 'pessimistic', whereas 'hopeful' means 'optimistic'.

17. stable
'stable' can mean 'a place where animals live' or 'firm'.

18. smart
'smart' can mean 'clever' or 'to hurt'.

19. tie
'tie' can mean 'an even score' or 'to join'.

20. handle
'handle' can mean 'something that is held' or 'to look after'.

21. keep
'keep' can mean 'a part of a fortress' or 'to hold on to something'.

22. petty
The other three mean 'hard to please'.

23. cage
The other three are all homes that animals build.

24. article
The other three are people who write articles.

25. darts
The other three are sports in which a ball (or balls) is used.

26. empty
The other three mean 'having lots of space'.

Test 28 — pages 104-107

1. B
Line 14 suggests that Groundhog Day might originate from a Christian festival, but the text doesn't say that this is what it is today. Line 2 mentions old wives' tales generally, rather than to describe Groundhog Day, and the last paragraph suggests that Punxsutawney Phil is unreliable at predicting the weather. However, lines 7-8 describe how people watch Phil annually, and lines 19-21 describe the large amount of interest in Groundhog Day, suggesting that it is a much-loved event.

2. D
The researchers state that Phil is correct around 40% of the time. This means that he is incorrect around 60% of the time, and so he is more likely to be incorrect than correct.

3. A
Lines 11-12 explain that if Phil "sees his own shadow" — meaning that it must be a sunny day — he returns to his burrow and there will be a longer winter. Therefore if February 2nd is a sunny day, Punxsutawney Phil predicts a longer winter.

4. C
Line 19 states that "it's Phil who remains the star", suggesting that Punxsutawney Phil is the most celebrated rodent.

5. D
Line 5 states that Groundhog Day takes place in Punxsutawney, Pennsylvania. Line 7 states that Groundhog Day was first celebrated in 1887, and line 8 states that the celebration takes place on 2nd February. The text does not mention why Groundhog Day is so popular in Pennsylvania.

6. A
'sophisticated' means 'refined'.

7. B
'undetermined' means 'unproven'.

8. stain
The other three are things that can cause stains.

9. bin
The other three are things that might be used to carry items.

10. fun
The other three describe someone who is looking forward to something.

11. chase
The other three mean 'to say someone is responsible for something'.

12. room
The other three are parts of a room.

13. advice
The other three mean 'to aid'.

14. succeed
The other three mean 'to talk in a self-satisfied way'.

15. tip
'tip' can mean 'to lean' or 'a piece of advice'.

16. fly
'fly' can mean 'a flying bug' or 'to sail through the air'.

17. bright
'bright' can mean 'intelligent' or 'shining'.

18. shower
'shower' can mean 'to wash under a jet of water' or 'a short period of rain'.

19. book
'book' can mean 'printed pages that are bound together' or 'to reserve something'.

20. fork
'fork' can mean 'a piece of cutlery' or 'a parting in a road'.

Puzzles 10 — page 108

Aliens are Landing!

The message is 'We will attack the Earthlings on Tuesday.'

Letter Lasso

conscious handsome opportunity rhythm occurred environment

Phrase: Howdy partner!

Test 29 — pages 109-111

1. bu**sy** — 'a **busy** European hub'
2. in**ha**bitants — 'over half a million **inhabitants**'
3. history — 'a turbulent **history**.'
4. struck — '**struck** by the plague'
5. population — 'a third of its **population**.'
6. destroyed — 'a fire **destroyed**'
7. without — '**without** homes.'
8. attacked — '**attacked** by British forces'
9. rebuilt — 'had to be **rebuilt**.'
10. peaceful — 'a lot more **peaceful**'
11. regularly — '**regularly** features'
12. live — 'in which to **live**.'

13. rocky
The other three mean 'granular'.

14. wing
The other three are a part of a human or animal's body used to walk on.

15. paper
The other three are parts of a piece of writing, rather than the material which a text is written on.

16. likely
The other three mean 'accurate'.

17. slippery
The other three are types of frozen water.

18. tap
'tap' can mean 'a light touch' or 'a valve from which water flows'.

19. slight
'slight' can mean 'petite' or 'small and unimportant'.

20. ring
'ring' can mean 'the peal of a bell' or 'a circular band'.

21. spoil
'spoil' can mean 'to go off' or 'to overindulge someone'.

22. board
'board' can mean 'a piece of wood' or 'to rent a living space'.

23. forgive
'blame' means 'to accuse', whereas 'forgive' means 'to pardon'.

24. ample
'meagre' means 'not enough', whereas 'ample' means 'plenty'.

25. valuable
'worthless' means 'of no value', whereas 'valuable' means 'precious'.

26. ashen
'tanned' means 'browned by the sun', whereas 'ashen' means 'pale'.

Test 30 — pages 112-115

1. C
The phrase "within barking distance" means that the foxes are near enough that their barks can be heard from the house. This suggests that they are close by.

2. B
In lines 4-5 the narrator states that they ran out of the house when they "heard the hens squawk".

3. B
Line 14 states that "the foxes possess the land at night", suggesting that they are nocturnal animals. The narrator also states that "No one would believe in the number of foxes" (line 2), suggesting that there are lots of foxes on the farm. During the day the foxes are said to "keep to their dens" (line 14). This suggests that a fox's home is called a den. Lines 16-17 state that "Foxes, like men, are more or less mechanical in their coming and going", suggesting that they behave predictably.

4. D
Line 9 states that the hen's weight of eight pounds is "a load" — meaning 'very heavy' — for the fox. The text also states that the hen was "squawking and flopping" to get away, and that the "tangle of brush and the steep hillside" was difficult terrain for the fox. The fox being trapped is not given as a reason why the fox didn't escape with the hen.

5. B
The narrator states that they heard the fox taking the hen during a "noon dinner" (line 4). 'Noon' is another word for midday.

6. C
'adjoining' means 'neighbouring'.

7. B
'boundaries' means 'confines'.

8. throw
'catch' means 'to grab', whereas 'throw' means 'to toss'.

9. dim
'bright' means 'emitting light', whereas 'dim' means 'quite dark'.

10. interesting
'boring' means 'dull', whereas 'interesting' means 'engaging'.

11. flatter
'belittle' means 'to criticise', whereas 'flatter' means 'to praise'.

12. smooth
'crease' means 'to fold', whereas 'smooth' means 'to straighten out'.

13. minor
'significant' means 'important', whereas 'minor' means 'not important'.

14. kittens
The words can be rearranged into the sentence 'The cat always runs through our garden.'

15. yesterday
The words can be rearranged into the sentence 'The supermarket was very busy last weekend.'

16. trip
The words can be rearranged into the sentence 'I sprained my wrist when I fell over.'

17. hammer
The words can be rearranged into the sentence 'Barney built the garden shed on his own.'

18. off
The words can be rearranged into the sentence 'Everyone leaves when the bell rings at noon.'

19. bake
The words can be rearranged into the sentence 'I put jam and butter on my scone.'

20. made
The words can be rearranged into the sentence 'I drink a cup of tea before I leave.'

Test 31 — pages 116-118

1. heard
'Have you ever **heard** someone'

2. This
'**This** type of language use'

3. thought
'it's **thought** to have originated'

4. exact
'its **exact** origins'

5. invented
'**invented** a rhyming code'

6. Another
'**Another** theory'

7. used
'it **used** to be popular'

8. mostly
'has now **mostly** fallen out of use'

9. However
'**However**, there are'

10. some
'there are **some** new slang terms'

11. recently
'emerged relatively **recently**'

12. trouble
"Barney Rubble' can mean '**trouble**'.'

13. top
'top' can mean 'the greatest' or 'a piece of clothing worn on the top half of the body'.

14. spring
'spring' can mean 'a place where water emerges from the ground' or 'to bounce'.

15. fit
'fit' can mean 'to belong' or 'in good physical shape'.

16. hound
'hound' can mean 'a dog' or 'to pursue'.

17. opening
'opening' can mean 'a gap' or 'the initial phase of something'.

18. dirt
The other three mean 'to rub something'.

19. October
The other three are measurements of time, rather than the name of a month.

20. lyrics
The other three are types of music.

21. couple
The other three are just one person.

22. country
The other three are places that are made up of groups of buildings.

23. uncommon
Both words mean 'unusual'.

24. imaginative
Both words mean 'inventive'.

25. task
Both words mean 'a job'.

26. amuse
Both words mean 'to captivate someone's attention'.

You have **10 minutes** to do this test. Work as quickly and accurately as you can.

Choose the correct words to complete the passage below.

The Empire State Building in New York is

1. ☐ single
☐ only
☐ sole
☐ one

of the most recognisable

buildings in the world. Surprisingly, it only took 410 days to

2. ☐ conclude
☐ complete
☐ end
☐ do

the

103-storey structure. The 204-ft mast situated at the top of the building is said to have

been designed to

3. ☐ allow
☐ give
☐ support
☐ tolerate

airships to dock, although some believe that it was

actually a way to

4. ☐ secure
☐ guard
☐ ensure
☐ protect

that the Empire State became the tallest building in the

world. Today, the mast is used to

5. ☐ post
☐ bring
☐ give
☐ broadcast

TV and radio across the city.

Although the building is

6. ☐ consists
☐ created
☐ made
☐ produced

up of offices, there are two

observation decks

7.
□ open
□ permit   to the
□ release
□ reveal

8.
□ person
□ communal
□ public   , from which, if the weather
□ society

9.
□ clear
is   □ stark   , you can see for up to 80 miles. Most people
□ free
□ simple

10.
□ go
□ do   the lift up
□ move
□ take

to these decks, but for the adventurous there's an

11.
□ yearly
□ regular
□ annual   race up the stairs
□ frequent

12.
□ ends
which   □ starts   at the ground floor and finishes on the 86th floor.
□ comes
□ from

Three of the words in each list are linked.
Mark the word that is not related to these three.

Example: red   green   ~~stripy~~   blue

---

13. scary   creepy   spooky   angry

14. door   house   chimney   window

15. pig   pup   calf   kitten

16. destroy   mend   shatter   demolish

17. museum   gallery   factory   library

Complete the word on the right so that it means the same, or nearly the same, as the word on the left.

Example: kind [c][a][r][i][n][g]

18. powerful   [s][ ][ ][o][n][ ]

19. startle   [s][ ][r][p][ ][i][s][ ]

20. bright   [i][ ][t][e][ ][l][i][ ][e][n][t]

21. teach   [ ][d][ ][c][ ][t][e]

Mark the word outside the brackets that has a similar meaning to the words in both sets of brackets.

Example: (circle ring)   (session game)   set   <u>round</u>   oval

22. (fill pack)   (things gear)   kit   cram   stuff

23. (juice lemonade) (gulp sip)   drink   beverage   swig

24. (cut chop)   (viewed watched)   knife   saw   observed

25. (king emperor)   (straightedge measure)   lord   ruler   inches

26. (mix blend)   (wake rouse)   join   mingle   stir

END OF TEST

/ 26

27

You have **10 minutes** to do this test. Work as quickly and accurately as you can.

Read this passage carefully and answer the questions that follow.

The Globe

In late 16th-century London, going to the theatre was a very popular pastime. By 1600, approximately 20 000 Londoners went to the theatre every week. So it's not surprising that playwrights like William Shakespeare were in high demand. Shakespeare didn't just write plays, he also performed in them too, most notably
5   in a theatrical company called The Lord Chamberlain's Men. In 1599, The Lord Chamberlain's Men constructed their own theatre — The Globe. Today, The Globe is synonymous with Shakespeare because many of his plays were first performed there.
The Globe was a circular structure, and although a roof covered some of the seating around the sides and the stage, the yard in the centre of the building was
10 open to the skies. The theatre was able to hold approximately 3000 people at any one time — the wealthier audience members usually sat in the covered seating, while the poorer audience members stood in the yard.
Unfortunately, during a performance of *Henry VIII* on the 29th June 1613, a cannon-based special effect set fire to the thatched roof of the theatre, and within
15 two hours the building had been razed to the ground. The theatre was rebuilt in haste and reopened just a year later, but this time it adopted a tiled roof instead of a thatched one. While Shakespeare may have performed at this theatre, it is doubtful that he wrote any plays for it. The new Globe stood for 30 years, until it was demolished to make room for housing.
20 It wasn't until 1997 that a third Globe was finally established near to the site of the original by American director Sam Wanamaker. Taking the name 'Shakespeare's Globe', this theatre is a very accurate representation of the original: it was built using similar materials and used 16th-century construction techniques. However, it can only hold audiences of half what it once could and has to adhere to strict modern
25 safety regulations.

Answer these questions about the text that you've just read.
Circle the letter that matches the correct answer.

1. Why is The Globe associated with Shakespeare?
   - **A**   It was destroyed during a performance of one of his plays.
   - **B**   Sam Wanamaker named his 1997 Globe theatre after him.
   - **C**   Many of his plays were first performed at the theatre.
   - **D**   He wrote a large number of plays.

2. Which of the following best describes the appearance of the original Globe?
   - **A**   A circular building with a tiled roof and a yard in the middle.
   - **B**   A circular building with a thatched roof and some seating.
   - **C**   A square building with no roof and a yard in the middle.
   - **D**   A square building with a tiled roof and some covered seating.

3. How many years had the original Globe been running before it was destroyed?
   - **A**   1 year
   - **B**   14 years
   - **C**   30 years
   - **D**   45 years

4. In what year was the second Globe theatre pulled down?
   - **A**   1613
   - **B**   1614
   - **C**   1643
   - **D**   1644

5. According to the text, which of the following statements must be true?

    A   Only the wealthy could afford to see plays in 17th-century London.

    B   Shakespeare's Globe was destroyed to make room for housing.

    C   In 1600, 20 000 people went to The Globe every week.

    D   Shakespeare was alive when the second Globe was constructed.

6. Approximately how many people can watch a performance at Shakespeare's Globe?

    A   750 people

    B   1500 people

    C   2250 people

    D   3000 people

7. According to the text, why is the third Globe not an exact copy of the original?

    A   The same building materials could not be sourced.

    B   It used modern construction techniques.

    C   It had to comply with new safety measures.

    D   It is twice the size of the original Globe.

In each question below, the words can be rearranged to form a sentence. One word doesn't fit in the sentence. Underline the word that doesn't fit.

Example: bus   the   <u>caught</u>   waited   the   boy   for

---

8. jokes   very   was   amusing   not   the   comedian

9. cereal   bowl   breakfast   eat   I   morning   every   for

10. in   mud   rolled   squeal   the   pig   around   the

11. went   a   Dougal   I   named   Labrador   had   black

12. the   on   money   once   floor   penny   found   a   I

13. to   taught   do   tricks   friend   how   amaze   himself   magic   my

14. was   I   slurp   so   the   drank   fountain   thirsty   of   I   out

---

Find the word that means the opposite, or nearly the opposite, of the word on the left.

Example: **love**   like   annoy   <u>hate</u>   enemy

---

15. **wet**   bare   hard   dry   moist

16. **capture**   hold   abandon   free   take

17. **fragile**   sturdy   flimsy   pretty   clumsy

18. **greed**   support   generosity   kindness   hospitality

19. **alarm**   steady   assist   calm   protect

20. **gradual**   rapid   slow   regular   prompt

END OF TEST

/ 20

Test 8

You have **10 minutes** to do this test. Work as quickly and accurately as you can.

Choose the correct words to complete the passage below.

Thomas Edison was an inventor who

1. ☐ clutched
    ☐ grasped
    ☐ held
    ☐ gripped

over 1000 patents for his

creations, and who made huge advancements in the field of electrical science.

As a

2. ☐ apprentice
    ☐ student
    ☐ observer
    ☐ educator

, Edison was

3. ☐ considered
    ☐ imagined
    ☐ suspected
    ☐ classed

disruptive. He only

4. ☐ spends
    ☐ spent
    ☐ spending
    ☐ spend

a short time at school before

5. ☐ being
    ☐ was
    ☐ went
    ☐ going

home-schooled by his

mother. Edison was a

6. ☐ sparkling
    ☐ shining
    ☐ bright
    ☐ blazing

child and had a thirst for knowledge.

Later in life, Edison worked on his own inventions and

7. ☐ usually
    ☐ occasionally
    ☐ definitely
    ☐ eventually

opened his own

8. ☐ investigate
    ☐ explore
    ☐ research
    ☐ analyse

facility. One of his most famous inventions is the

32

9. ☐ allowed
   ☐ released
   ☐ charged
   ☐ yielded

phonograph, which   people to record sound and play it back.

10. ☐ Whilst
    ☐ Regardless
    ☐ Despite   this innovation is remarkable, Edison is most commonly
    ☐ However

11. ☐ combined   12. ☐ helped
    ☐ united   ☐ maintained
    ☐ joined   with the light bulb, which   ☐ supported   to make lighting
    ☐ associated   ☐ assisted

safer and more affordable.

In each question below, the words can be rearranged to form a sentence.
One word doesn't fit in the sentence. Underline the word that doesn't fit.

Example: bus   the   <u>caught</u>   waited   the   boy   for

---

13. some   adopted   few   neighbour   recently   kittens   my

14. lemurs   on   habitat   of   island   most   the   Madagascar   live

15. calculator   Lynette   not   maths   very   was   good   at

16. way   skids   on   I   my   ice   on   home   slipped   the

Mark the word outside the brackets that has a similar meaning to the words in both sets of brackets.

Example: (circle ring) (session game)   set <u>round</u> oval

17. (curvy twisty)   (gusty breezy)   wavy   blustery   windy

18. (follow pursue)   (twig trunk)   stalk   reed   ambush

19. (jacket anorak)   (cover paint)   apply   cape   coat

20. (ripped damaged) (undecided unsure)   uncertain   torn   ruined

21. (treasure booty)   (steal rob)   raid   haul   loot

Complete the word on the right so that it means the opposite, or nearly the opposite, of the word on the left.

Example: start   [e][n][d]

22. add   [s][ ][b][ ][r][ ][c][t]

23. dawdle   [h][ ][ ][r][ ]

24. humble   [b][o][ ][s][ ][ ][ ][l]

25. unwilling [ ][a][g][ ][r]

26. encourage [d][ ][t][ ][r]

END OF TEST

/ 26

Puzzles 3

Have a break and practise your **word-making** skills with these puzzles.

Word Ladder

First, solve the clues to find the words. Then add the words to the ladder in the right order.

Each word on the ladder has had one letter changed from the word on the rung below. (e.g. B**E**AT might become B**O**AT).

a) A place where waste water goes.

    _ _ _ _ _

b) To move around on your hands and knees.

    _ _ _ _ _

c) Something you use to solve this puzzle!

    _ _ _ _ _

d) A verb meaning 'to speak in a slow and lazy way'.   _ _ _ _ _

e) An adjective meaning 'pale and tired'.

    _ _ _ _ _

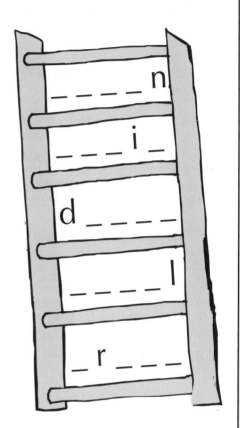

Forwards Backwards

Solve these riddles to find four words that mean something different when they are spelled backwards.

a) Forwards I'm like hay. Backwards I am lumpy.   _ _ _ _ _ W

b) Forwards I'm part of a bag. Backwards I'm in pieces.   S _ _ _ _ _

c) Forwards I give light. Backwards I weep.   _ _ L _

d) Forwards I'm a glimpse. Backwards I hold on to something.   _ E _ _ _

35

You have **10 minutes** to do this test. Work as quickly and accurately as you can.

Fill in the missing letters to complete the words in the following passage.

1. Tea is a very popular d ⬚ i ⬚ k in Britain, with 165 million cups being

2. drunk every day. It's made from the dried, crushed l e ⬚ v ⬚ ⬚ of the

3. *Camellia sinensis* plant, which g ⬚ ⬚ w ⬚ in countries with a warm,

4. humid c l ⬚ ⬚ ⬚ t e. When hot water is added to the leaves, it

5. becomes infused with their f ⬚ ⬚ v ⬚ u r. It's unclear how the drink

6. of tea was invented, but one e x ⬚ l a ⬚ a t ⬚ o ⬚ comes from

7. a Chinese l e ⬚ e n ⬚. About 4500 years ago, the Emperor Shennong

8. is said to have been boiling water when a leaf from a ⬚ ⬚ ⬚ r b y shrub

9. fell into the cup, a c c ⬚ ⬚ e n ⬚ a l ⬚ y creating the first

10. cup of tea. Some countries also have special r ⬚ t ⬚ a l ⬚ around

11. drinking tea — in Japan, for example, tea c e r ⬚ ⬚ o n ⬚ e s

12. involve particular r u ⬚ ⬚ s about how to pour and drink the tea.

Three of the words in each list are linked.
Mark the word that is not related to these three.

Example: red   green   <u>stripy</u>   blue

13. planet   rocket   star   moon

14. forest   cavern   cave   cliff

15. pen   pencil   eraser   crayon

16. exercising   running   swimming   cycling

17. oily   greasy   slippery   soggy

Complete the word on the right so that it means the same, or nearly the same, as the word on the left.

Example: kind   [c][a][r][i]n[g]

18. quiet   [p][ ][a][c][ ][ ][u][l]

19. scatter   [s][ ][r][ ][a][d]

20. busy   [b][u][ ][t][l][ ][n][ ]

21. basic   [ ][i][ ][p][ ][e]

22. think   [c][o][ ][s][ ][ ][e][r]

In each question below, the words can be rearranged to form a sentence.
One word doesn't fit in the sentence. Underline the word that doesn't fit.

Example: bus   the   <u>caught</u>   waited   the   boy   for

23. mum   was   nurse   Oliver's   a   veterinary   animals

24. my   missed   minutes   London   train   I   to   yesterday

25. children   havoc   in   the   caused   ball   swam   the   pool

26. ordered   me   what   taste   I   waiter   give   not   did   the

END OF TEST

/ 26

You have **10 minutes** to do this test. Work as quickly and accurately as you can.

Read this passage carefully and answer the questions that follow.

An abridged extract from 'The Old House'

In the street, up there, was an old, a very old house — it was almost three hundred years old, for that might be known by reading the great beam on which the date of the year was carved: together with tulips and hop-binds*, […] and over every window was a distorted face cut out in the beam. The one storey stood forward a
5   great way over the other; and directly under the eaves was a leaden** spout with a dragon's head; the rain-water should have run out of the mouth, but it ran out of the belly, for there was a hole in the spout.

All the other houses in the street were so new and so neat, with large window panes and smooth walls, one could easily see that they would have nothing to do
10   with the old house: they certainly thought, "How long is that old decayed thing to stand here as a spectacle in the street? And then the projecting windows stand so far out, that no one can see from our windows what happens in that direction! The steps are as broad as those of a palace, and as high as to a church tower. The iron railings look just like the door to an old family vault***, and then they have brass tops —
15   that's so stupid!"

On the other side of the street were also new and neat houses, and they thought just as the others did; but at the window opposite the old house there sat a little boy with fresh rosy cheeks and bright beaming eyes: he certainly liked the old house best, and that both in sunshine and moonshine.

Hans Christian Andersen

* hop-binds — *plant stalks*
** leaden — *made of lead*
*** vault — *a chamber where the dead can be buried*

Answer these questions about the text that you've just read.
Circle the letter that matches the correct answer.

1. Which of the following best describes the majority of the houses on the street?

    A   Small and cosy

    B   Plain and basic

    C   Tidy and small

    D   Modern and well-kept

2. Which of the following is not given in the text?

    A   What year the old house was built

    B   What is carved into the great beam

    C   What is carved above the old house's windows

    D   Which house the little boy preferred

3. According to the text, why do the windows in the old house cause a problem?

    A   They don't match the other windows on the street.

    B   They block the view from the other houses.

    C   The window panes are too large.

    D   The window frames are rotten.

4. According to the text, which of the following statements is false?

    A   The house has broken guttering.

    B   The house has at least two levels.

    C   There is a single row of houses on the street.

    D   Most of the houses on the street are new.

5. Which of the following does not describe the house?

    A   It has brass railings.

    B   It has high steps.

    C   It has wide steps.

    D   Its gutters are made from lead.

6. What does "decayed" (line 10) mean?

    A   Rotten

    B   Unpleasant

    C   Ancient

    D   Ugly

7. What does "distorted" (line 4) mean?

    A   Aged

    B   Scary

    C   Rusty

    D   Misshapen

Complete the word on the right so that it means the opposite, or nearly the opposite, of the word on the left.

Example: start   e n d

---

8. edge   m ☐ d d ☐ ☐

9. healthy   a ☐ l ☐ n g

10. delighted   s a d ☐ ☐ n ☐ d

11. polite   s ☐ r ☐ y

12. spicy   ☐ ☐ a ☐ d

13. dry   j ☐ ☐ c ☐

14. wither   ☐ l o ☐ m

Three of the words in each list are linked.
Mark the word that is not related to these three.

Example: red   green   <u>stripy</u>   blue

15. gold   platinum   silver   metal

16. feathers   cotton   fur   hair

17. painting   sketch   writing   picture

18. brother   friend   nephew   aunt

19. origin   start   beginning   result

20. acceptance   freedom   release   liberty

END OF TEST

/ 20

Have a go at these puzzles — they're a great way to practise your **word-finding** skills.

Build the Pyramid

Add either a prefix or a suffix to each word below. Use the prefixes <u>re-</u> or <u>in-</u>, or the suffixes <u>-ful</u> or <u>-able</u>.

Put the new words in the correct spaces to complete the pyramid.

a. admire

b. use

c. joy

d. complete

e. definite

f. believe

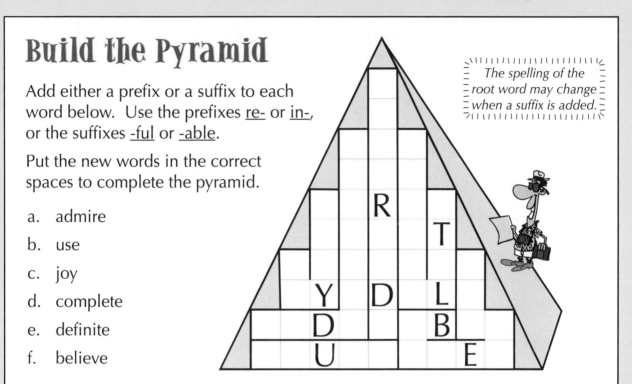

The spelling of the root word may change when a suffix is added.

Hidden Words

In each sentence a four-letter word is hidden at the end of one word and the start of the next. Underline the letters that contain the hidden word. The **last letter** of each word you've found can be rearranged into a synonym for 'happy'.

Example: <u>The m</u>an stood up and asked a question.

1. Twins who look exactly alike are known as identical twins.

2. After much trouble, Liu managed to close her window.

3. Joe had found a way to make himself invisible.

4. My uncle's hairy ears help him to hear better.

5. The train must arrive on time or we will be late.

A synonym of **happy**:

_ _ _ _ _

You have **10 minutes** to do this test. Work as quickly and accurately as you can.

Fill in the missing letters to complete the words in the following passage.

1.   A p r ☐ ☐ n a ☐ t frog will usually lay her eggs in water

2.   or somewhere m ☐ ☐ i s ☐ . As she lays the eggs, they are

3.   fertilised by a male frog. These eggs f ☐ ☐ r ☐ a clump which floats on

4.   the s ☐ r f ☐ c ☐ of the water and is known as frogspawn.

5.   The female frog will lay a large n ☐ ☐ b e ☐ of eggs — up to 20 000 —

6.   this is because only a few will s ☐ ☐ ☐ v i ☐ ☐ into adulthood.

7.   Although the eggs are protected by a jelly-like s u ☐ s t ☐ n c ☐ ,

8.   the majority of eggs will be killed by predators or d ☐ s e a ☐ ☐ s .

9.   From the eggs, tadpoles will h ☐ ☐ c h — tiny creatures with

10. long tails which e ☐ ☐ b l ☐ them to swim easily in the water.

11. After this, the tadpole will d ☐ v ☐ l ☐ p lungs and become a

12. f ☐ ☐ l y grown frog.

44

Mark the word outside the brackets that has a similar meaning to the words in both sets of brackets.

Example: (circle ring) (session game)   set <u>round</u> oval

13. (hot toasty)   (friendly kind)   nice warm baking

14. (desire wish)   (illusion fantasy)   dream hope mirage

15. (painting sketch) (visualise imagine)   picture see illustration

16. (excuse pardon) (additional excess)   release extra spare

17. (heath pasture) (fasten tie)   field secure moor

In each question below, the words can be rearranged to form a sentence. One word doesn't fit in the sentence. Underline the word that doesn't fit.

Example: bus the <u>caught</u> waited the boy for

18. ball play the was out the said umpire

19. dentist had Martin the brace an with appointment

20. started to fitness my improve pools I swimming have

21. with happy friend exams was results my test her

22. received Christmas is I jumper really a itchy present for

Find the word that means the opposite, or nearly the opposite, of the word on the left.

Example: **love**   like   annoy   <u>hate</u>   enemy

23. **true**   insincere   false   wrong   incorrect

24. **freeze**   dissolve   chill   thaw   chop

25. **guard**   prisoner   criminal   warden   culprit

26. **careful**   silly   cautious   reckless   happy

END OF TEST

/ 26

You have **10 minutes** to do this test. Work as quickly and accurately as you can.

Read this passage carefully and answer the questions that follow.

The Amazon Rainforest

From dense jungle to thick woodland, forests cover a large portion of our
planet. The largest tropical rainforest is the Amazon Rainforest, which is located
in the Amazon River Basin, an area of South America. The Amazon Rainforest is
approximately half the size of the United States, over twenty times the size of
5   the UK, and contains about half of all the tropical rainforest on Earth. The word
'Amazon' is also commonly associated with the river that runs through the rainforest.
At over 6400 km, the Amazon River is the second-longest river in the world.

The Amazon Rainforest is home to at least 10% of all the known species on
our planet and is incredibly biodiverse*. Surveys suggest that the Amazon houses
10   approximately 2.5 million insect species, 40 000 species of plant, over 400 species
of mammals, 400 species of reptile and a combined total of around 24 000 species of
trees, fish, birds and amphibians. Even so, scientists believe many of the rainforest's
species remain unknown and unclassified. Although the variety of life is astounding,
not all inhabitants of the Amazon Rainforest are friendly. Deadly jaguars and snakes
15   roam the forest floor, and even inconspicuous mosquitoes carry diseases such as
malaria and yellow fever.

The Amazon Rainforest is also an important contributor to the health of the human
race and the planet. Its vegetation has been the source of many medical advances,
and it also helps stabilise Earth's climate. The Amazon is often called 'The Lungs
20   of the Planet' because its plant life produces about 20% of the world's oxygen
while absorbing carbon dioxide from the atmosphere. Deforestation, however, has
lessened the effect of this 'carbon sink'. Approximately 20% of the rainforest has
been destroyed in the last fifty years, which is partly due to growing crops and the
construction of cattle ranches. Deforestation has also caused the destruction of
25   animal habitats, and every day multiple species become extinct.

* biodiverse — *having a lot of different species of plants and animals*

Answer these questions about the text that you've just read.
Circle the letter that matches the correct answer.

1. According to the text, which of the following statements is true?

   A   The Amazon Rainforest is located in the United States.

   B   The Amazon Rainforest contains more species than we know about.

   C   The Amazon River Basin is located in the Amazon Rainforest.

   D   The Amazon River Basin contains at least 10% of all life on Earth.

2. Which of the following isn't mentioned in the text?

   A   Mosquitoes can carry malaria.

   B   Deforestation of the Amazon has led to the extinction of some animals.

   C   A river flows through the Amazon Rainforest.

   D   Humans are unable to survive in the Amazon Rainforest.

3. According to the text, which of the following does the Amazon have the most of?

   A   Mammal species

   B   Reptile species

   C   Tree species

   D   It is not clear from the text.

4. Why is the Amazon Rainforest called "The Lungs of the Planet" (lines 19-20)?

   A   It is shaped like a pair of lungs.

   B   Vegetation found in the Amazon helps people with breathing problems.

   C   It produces 20% of the world's oxygen and absorbs carbon dioxide.

   D   It is home to thousands of living things.

5. According to the text, which of the following statements is false?

    A   The Amazon Rainforest is the largest tropical rainforest in the world.

    B   The USA is more than 20 times the size of the UK.

    C   The longest river in the world is over 6400 km.

    D   Cattle farming has destroyed around 20% of the Amazon Rainforest.

6. What does "astounding" (line 13) mean?

    A   Unsurprising

    B   Amazing

    C   Alarming

    D   Unimaginable

7. What does "stabilise" (line 19) mean?

    A   Maintain

    B   Improve

    C   Monitor

    D   Purge

In each question below, the words can be rearranged to form a sentence. One word doesn't fit in the sentence. Underline the word that doesn't fit.

    Example: bus   the   <u>caught</u>   waited   the   boy   for

---

8. baby   ate   tried   the   reach   the   plum   to

9. his   the   snapped   jaws   in   alligator   anger   splash

10. drink   my   spilt   I   the   accidentally   on   floor   them

11. for   extra   burger   my   I   asked   fast   on   cheese

12. wind lake go the on Cathy sailing to liked

13. the book her read girl tree the oak under shade

14. scared when off dark bedroom was his Eric turned light was

Complete the word on the right so that it means the same, or nearly the same, as the word on the left.

Example: kind   [c][a][r][i][n][g]

15. broken   [ ][a][m][ ][ ][e][d]

16. choose   [s][ ][l][ ][c][ ]

17. funny   [ ][i][ ][a][r][ ][o][ ][s]

18. sound   [n][ ][i][ ][e]

19. act   [p][ ][r][ ][o][ ][m]

20. brave   [c][o][ ][r][ ][g][e][ ][u][s]

END OF TEST

/ 20

You have **10 minutes** to do this test. Work as quickly and accurately as you can.

Read this passage carefully and answer the questions that follow.

Tunnel Vision

Coming from a small, rural community, I'd never been to the British capital before. I was familiar with London's transport system, however, since red double-deckers and black cabs seem to be almost as iconic as the Union Jack. The change from my village to the intricate labyrinth of London was a culture shock, but it was the
5   Underground that intimidated me most.

I'm quite claustrophobic, so the word 'Tube' is enough to strike fear into my heart, never mind the thought of being inside one. I wanted to avoid it if possible, but my friend assured me that it was the fastest way to get around, and would be vital if we wanted to accomplish everything we had planned.
10   So, I reluctantly agreed to venture into the dark unknown for the sake of practicality. Jake had already bought me a ticket, and as soon as we went below ground, I was carried along by a wave of people. Everyone appeared to have developed the most efficient method of getting through the ticket barriers. People simply waved their cards and the gates opened. I clumsily inserted my ticket
15   multiple times before the barrier granted me access, while a queue of people formed behind me.

Jake suggested that I stick to the right of the escalator. I didn't understand why until a man flew past me on the left, darting down the steps like he was about to break into a sprint. Being used to a more sedate way of life, it baffled me why
20   everyone was in such a rush.

As Jake proceeded through the tunnels, I glimpsed the Tube map, but all I could see was a series of coloured lines snaking around one another in an unfathomable mess. As the sea of people veered off in different directions, I concluded that the best thing to do was simply follow Jake; it was all too complicated for me.

Answer these questions about the text that you've just read.
Circle the letter that matches the correct answer.

1. According to the text, where does the narrator live?

    A   A village in the Scottish Highlands

    B   A farming community in northern England

    C   A rural hamlet in the south of England

    D   It is unclear from the text

2. The narrator describes the visit to London as a "culture shock" (line 4). This means:

    A   they are impressed by London's iconic public transport.

    B   they are shocked by the number of museums and galleries in London.

    C   they find London unfamiliar and disorientating.

    D   they struggle to navigate their way around London.

3. Why is the narrator reluctant to take the Underground?

    A   Operating the ticket barriers is a complicated process.

    B   The narrator doesn't understand the Underground map.

    C   The narrator dislikes being in confined spaces.

    D   The narrator dislikes being in the dark.

4. Which of the following words best describes how the narrator feels in lines 12-16?

    A   Ashamed

    B   Flustered

    C   Competent

    D   Unintelligent

5. Which of the following best explains the narrator's attitude to the Underground map?

    A   It seems easy to understand.

    B   It seems very confusing.

    C   It seems poorly designed.

    D   It seems extremely interesting.

6. What does "vital" (line 8) mean?

    A   Suitable

    B   Necessary

    C   Optional

    D   Useful

7. What does "sedate" (line 19) mean?

    A   Rural

    B   Calm

    C   Boring

    D   Refined

Find the word that means the same, or nearly the same, as the word on the left.

    Example: **tub**   flask <u>pot</u> bottle glass

---

8. **gentle**   cautious lovely feeble delicate

9. **lock**   grasp clench latch press

10. **vanish**   disappear change fade melt

11. **ramp**   bend uneven incline twist

12. **rest**   peace   pause   silence   ease

13. **reason**   apology   alibi   explanation   regret

14. **request**   command   challenge   investigate   ask

Three of the words in each list are linked.
Mark the word that is not related to these three.

Example: red   green   <u>stripy</u>   blue

---

15. trumpet   clarinet   guitar   flute

16. table   bench   sofa   armchair

17. water   glass   jug   bottle

18. shrub   hedge   fence   bush

19. doctor   nurse   surgeon   medicine

20. illustrate   complicate   show   demonstrate

END OF TEST

/ 20

Puzzles 5

Time for a break! This puzzle is a great way to practise your **word-making** skills.

Picture Words

Each of the nine boxes below contains a clue.

Use these clues to write down nine words or phrases. An example is shown to the right.

Half of each answer is written in the clue — the other half is the way the clue is presented.

D
N
U
O
R
....
round-up

_____

_____

_____

DATE
_____

_____

_____

_____

_____

_____

Test 15

You have **10 minutes** to do this test. Work as quickly and accurately as you can.

Choose the correct words to complete the passage below.

The Iron Age in Britain was a
1. ☐ year
☐ period
☐ century
☐ decade
from about 800 BC to 43 AD, after

the Bronze Age and
2. ☐ previous
☐ prior
☐ before
☐ follow
the Romans invaded. Iron Age people usually

3. ☐ owned
☐ stayed
☐ visited
☐ lived
in roundhouses in small
4. ☐ fields
☐ acres
☐ expanses
☐ villages
or larger towns.

Building a roundhouse
5. ☐ was
☐ be
☐ could
☐ should
quite complex. Firstly, the space for the

house — which was usually just a single circular room —
6. ☐ would
☐ have
☐ had
☐ will
to be marked

out. Wooden stakes and woven 'wattle' would form the walls. A large thatched roof

56

© CGP — not to be photocopied

7. □ slept
   □ paused
   □ rested   on wooden beams, which
   □ holding

8. □ balanced
   □ placed
   □ extended   into the centre of
   □ supported

9. □ Nearly
   □ Lately
   □ Closely   , the walls were plastered with daub, which was
   □ Finally

the structure.

10. □ made
    □ mixed
    □ found   of clay, water, straw and cow dung. Daub
    □ combined

11. □ indicated
    □ ensured
    □ helped
    □ made

the house to retain heat, and provided some

12. □ protection
    □ defended
    □ assistance   from the weather.
    □ break

In each question below, the words can be rearranged to form a sentence.
One word doesn't fit in the sentence. Underline the word that doesn't fit.

Example: bus   the   <u>caught</u>   waited   the   boy   for

---

13. was   outside   go   weather   and   the   stormy   dark

14. a   meal   family   for   the   delicious   restaurant   out   went

15. Trevor   baking   followed   never   but   kitchen   recipe   liked   the

16. views   there   really   in   countryside   are   the   sight   stunning

Find the word that means the opposite, or nearly the opposite, of the word on the left.

Example: **love**   like   annoy   <u>hate</u>   enemy

17. **ceiling**   floor   wall   storey   cellar

18. **arrogant**   polite   modest   sad   unhappy

19. **sticky**   slippery   scratchy   glossy   soft

20. **straight**   bumpy   crooked   parallel   messy

21. **involve**   forget   neglect   join   exclude

Three of the words in each list are linked.
Mark the word that is not related to these three.

Example: red   green   <u>stripy</u>   blue

22. sink   boost   rise   increase

23. square   rectangle   triangle   shape

24. French   Germany   Spanish   Italian

25. mix   blend   chop   stir

26. shriek   yell   squeal   tickle

END OF TEST

/ 26

You have **10 minutes** to do this test. Work as quickly and accurately as you can.

Read this passage carefully and answer the questions that follow.

Campfire Story

It had been a long, hot day of hill walking, and everyone had begun to settle down around the small, flaming campfire. It would have been nice to have lit it during the daylight, but after an argument had sparked between Jenna and Marcus over how best to create the fire, it was just a relief to have it burning. Beth had
5   used her phone as a torch, allowing the pair to see what they were doing. When the artificial light was finally extinguished, all we could see was the fire blazing brightly and our faces illuminated in orange light.

Throughout my childhood, I had only associated fire with destruction, never fully appreciating the good it can bring. Fire is certainly dangerous and must be handled
10 with care, but as we hovered around it like moths I could not help but thank it for the light, warmth and food it had provided us with. After we had finished gorging on piping hot sausages, Jenna surprised us with a bag of marshmallows, which we immediately started roasting on the fire.

We sat by the campfire with only the crackling of embers, the whispers of nature
15 and the sound of the cow in the next field for company. When the conversation lulled, there was an eerie silence. Karim decided that we should share scary stories in an attempt to spook ourselves. Personally, these tales did nothing to make me feel uneasy, but I enjoyed the atmosphere anyway. Marcus, however, drifted off halfway through Beth's story about a zombie hitchhiker. Although his snores ruined
20 the mood, they signalled that it was probably time for us to get into our sleeping bags and call it a night.

Answer these questions about the text that you've just read.
Circle the letter that matches the correct answer.

1. Which of the following best describes why the narrator wanted to light the campfire earlier?

    A   So they could enjoy the fire for longer

    B   So they could build the campfire when it was light

    C   So they could roast the marshmallows sooner

    D   So they could sit around it and tell ghost stories

2. Which of the following statements must be true?

    A   The group go camping during the summer.

    B   Jenna brought a torch with her.

    C   The group cook food on the campfire.

    D   Moths were attracted to the light of the campfire.

3. Lines 15-16 state that the "conversation lulled". This means:

    A   the conversation became boring for a moment.

    B   the conversation was sad for a moment.

    C   the conversation became scary for a moment.

    D   the conversation stopped for a moment.

4. According to the passage, how many people took part in the camping trip?

    A   Three

    B   Four

    C   Five

    D   Six

5. Which of the following best describes the narrator's attitude to the ghost stories?

    A   He found them scary, and they made him feel uneasy.

    B   He thought they were boring, and they made him fall asleep.

    C   He didn't find them scary, but he liked the mood they created.

    D   He found them chilling, but he enjoyed listening to them anyway.

6. What does "artificial" (line 6) mean?

    A   Bright

    B   Dim

    C   Glowing

    D   Unnatural

7. What does "eerie" (line 16) mean?

    A   Unsettling

    B   Terrifying

    C   Unexpected

    D   Comfortable

Mark the word outside the brackets that has a similar meaning to the words in both sets of brackets.

Example: (circle ring) (session game)   set   <u>round</u>   oval

---

8. (pole stake)   (letter card)   mail   post   plank

9. (bird fowl)   (bend crouch)   goose   duck   dodge

10. (source spring) (hearty healthy)   fountain   fit   well

         Test 16

11. (delicate thin)   (okay alright)   flimsy   average   fine

12. (beach shore)   (cruise drift)   sail   coast   cliff

13. (miserable sad)   (overcast dull)   murky   upset   gloomy

14. (see identify)   (blemish pimple)   mole   spot   recognise

---

In each question below, the words can be rearranged to form a sentence.
One word doesn't fit in the sentence. Underline the word that doesn't fit.

Example: bus   the   <u>caught</u>   waited   the   boy   for

---

15. books   same   at   Rose   several   reading   once   was

16. Lizzie   incredibly   has   pugs   love   strong   an   adores   of

17. it   because   frozen   wore   chilly   my   coat   was   I

18. was   be   Lauren's   play   dream   a   to   audience   in

19. ran   to   walk   school   his   Jeremy   on   had   own   to

20. showed   the   office   man   help   the   us   to   way   the

END OF TEST

/ 20

Puzzles 6

There are two puzzles on this page that are bound to give your brain a workout.

Antonym Anagrams

Five words are hidden in the grid.

Solve each anagram, and then find its antonym in the wordsearch.

Example: c i k u q   *quick*

a) g h l t i   _____

b) r u g y h n   _____

c) s w r n e a   _____

d) z e f e e r   _____

e) l e u s p a e r   _____

N	M	E	L	T	D	U	S
O	I	J	N	Y	H	T	A
I	P	F	U	R	E	T	D
T	R	U	V	X	A	Y	N
S	E	L	G	W	V	L	E
E	E	L	I	H	Y	E	S
U	H	B	S	L	O	W	S
Q	C	B	S	K	R	E	T

Shuffled Sentences

Underline the two words in each sentence that should be swapped in order for each sentence to make sense.

Use one of the swapped words from each sentence to finish the sentence about what happened when Miya brought her pet dinosaur to school.

1. Excited was everyone to see the band at the concert.

2. After the discussion, we elected Sidra to be some leader for our team.

3. Having seen the them play, I thought I would congratulate team.

4. Diana as she turned the corner, just remembered to fetch her lunch.

"1) _____ screamed, and 2) _____ ran away,

until I told 3) _____ that he 4) _____ wanted to play!"

You have **10 minutes** to do this test. Work as quickly and accurately as you can.

Fill in the missing letters to complete the words in the following passage.

1.   Galileo Galilei was b☐☐☐ near Pisa, Italy in 1564. Although he

2.   s t ☐ ☐ i e ☐ philosophy and mathematics at university, he is

3.   mainly r ☐ m ☐ ☐ b e ☐ e d for his contributions to astronomy.

4.   Galileo heard about the i n v ☐ ☐ t ☐ o n of the telescope in 1609.

5.   He built a better v ☐ ☐ r s ☐ ☐ n — even though he'd never seen

6.   the original — and used it to look at stars and planets. T ☐ ☐ o u ☐ h

7.   observation, he came to b ☐ l i ☐ ☐ e that the Sun was the centre of

8.   our Solar System, rather than the Earth, as most p ☐ ☐ ☐ p l ☐ thought

9.   at the time. Galileo tried to publicise his f i ☐ d ☐ ☐ g s , but

10. because they were so controversial, he was ☐ ☐ n n e ☐ from talking

11. about them, and he was put under house ☐ r r ☐ s t . Although

12. Galileo's genius wasn't fully appreciated in his l ☐ f ☐ t ☐ m e ,

     he paved the way for modern astronomy.

Three of the words in each list are linked.
Mark the word that is not related to these three.

Example: red   green   <u>stripy</u>   blue

13. month   afternoon   evening   morning

14. oppose   disagree   protest   accept

15. mouth   nose   face   lips

16. brush   artist   canvas   paint

17. drought   hurricane   typhoon   monsoon

Find the word that means the same, or nearly the same, as the word on the left.

Example: **tub**   flask   <u>pot</u>   bottle   glass

18. **quiet**   dull   silence   gentle   eerie

19. **scary**   bizarre   creepy   mysterious   scream

20. **pull**   load   shove   move   yank

21. **distant**   secret   obscure   faraway   inaccessible

22. **obedient**   tame   caring   well-behaved   honourable

                                       Test 17

Mark the word outside the brackets that has a similar meaning to the words in both sets of brackets.

Example: (circle ring)   (session game)   set   <u>round</u>   oval

23. (slant tilt)   (skinny slim)   lean   thin   angle

24. (preserve spread) (cram stuff)   marmalade   jam   wedge

25. (touch stroke)   (think believe)   consider   clasp   feel

26. (skin fur)   (disguise cover)   smuggle   wool   hide

END OF TEST

/ 26

You have **10 minutes** to do this test. Work as quickly and accurately as you can.

Read this passage carefully and answer the questions that follow.

Queen Nefertiti

People have always been fascinated by ancient civilisations, and ancient Egypt is no exception. While modern technology and research have allowed us to solve some of ancient Egypt's mysteries, there are still unanswered questions. One of ancient Egypt's most enigmatic figures is Queen Nefertiti, who married Pharaoh
5   Akhenaten.

In 1912, a German archaeologist discovered a bust* of the Queen. The bust is an exceptional example of ancient Egyptian craftsmanship, and thanks to the sculptor's depiction of the Queen, some people have heralded her as one of the most beautiful women of all time, even though the bust is missing an eye. Nefertiti also features
10   on other artworks of the period. She is often depicted alongside her husband and children, but she also appears riding chariots, defeating enemies and leading worship.

Despite these surviving artworks, much of Nefertiti's life is shrouded in uncertainty. She is commonly believed to be the daughter of a royal advisor, and
15   subsequent Pharaoh of Egypt, called Ay, but some historians claim she was a princess from Syria. Around the twelfth year of Akhenaten's reign, Nefertiti seemingly disappears. Her disappearance remains a highly debated topic. Some believe that she died; others believe she was outcast for religious reasons. One theory even states that Nefertiti changed her name and ruled as co-regent** of Egypt.
20   Nefertiti's final resting place has yet to be identified, although recent archaeological discoveries suggest she may be buried in a secret chamber of Tutankhamun's*** tomb. Whatever is unearthed in the future, Nefertiti will remain one of the most recognisable faces of ancient Egypt.

* bust — *sculpture of a person's head and shoulders*
** co-regent — *joint ruler*
*** Tutankhamun — *a famous Egyptian pharaoh*

1. Which of the following words wouldn't be used to describe how Nefertiti was depicted in ancient Egyptian artworks?

   A   Mysterious

   B   Beautiful

   C   Powerful

   D   Religious

2. According to the text, which of the following statements must be true?

   A   Nefertiti was a Syrian princess.

   B   Nefertiti only had one eye.

   C   Ay was a Syrian king.

   D   Akhenaten reigned for more than a decade.

3. Which of the following facts is given in the text?

   A   The country in which Nefertiti was born.

   B   The name of the German archaeologist who discovered the bust.

   C   The place where Nefertiti's remains were found.

   D   The name of Nefertiti's husband.

4. According to the text, which of the following is the most mysterious aspect of Nefertiti's life?

   A   Who her father was

   B   Why she appears in so many artworks

   C   What happened to her in later life

   D   Why she was buried in Tutankhamun's tomb

5. According to the text, which of the following statements must be true?

    A   Nefertiti was the most beautiful woman of all time.

    B   Nefertiti's bust was discovered in Germany.

    C   Nefertiti was a mother.

    D   Nefertiti changed her name when she became co-regent.

6. What does "exceptional" (line 7) mean?

    A   Adequate

    B   Inspirational

    C   Strange

    D   Extraordinary

7. What does "subsequent" (line 15) mean?

    A   Popular

    B   Powerful

    C   Later

    D   Prior

Three of the words in each list are linked.
Mark the word that is not related to these three.

    Example: red   green   <u>stripy</u>   blue

8. foggy   misty   hazy   windy

9. cake   tart   cook   pie

10. trim   extend   stretch   lengthen

11. wicked   beast   fiend   monster

12. passenger   deckhand   steward   captain

13. glint   explosion   flicker   flash

Find the word that means the same, or nearly the same, as the word on the left.

Example: **tub**   flask   <u>pot</u>   bottle   glass

---

14. **fortunate**   peaceful   happy   lucky   merry

15. **dupe**   fake   joke   disguise   trick

16. **soak**   spray   drench   cover   wash

17. **event**   adventure   story   occasion   feud

18. **argue**   squabble   brawl   riot   battle

19. **nutritious**   delicious   healthy   clean   fresh

20. **disturb**   obstruct   disconnect   prevent   disrupt

END OF TEST

/ 20

You have **10 minutes** to do this test. Work as quickly and accurately as you can.

Fill in the missing letters to complete the words in the following passage.

1. Some people might [s][ ][g][ ][ ][s][ ] that building sandcastles

2. is a childish [a][ ][t][ ][v][i][t][ ], but for others, it's an art form.

3. It takes a [s][ ][ ][a][ ][y] hand and lots of concentration to build a

4. sculpture out of sand, but the results are often [e][l][ ][ ][o][r][ ][t][e]

5. and impressive. It can take many [ ][o][u][ ][s] to build a sand sculpture,

6. so the [a][ ][t][i][ ][ ] will pick a spot away from the water's edge

7. to protect their artwork from the [i][ ][c][o][ ][ ][n][g] tide.

8. Several [ ][ ][ ][s][ ][d][e] towns in the UK hold sand sculpture

9. competitions during the summer months, which [ ][l][l][ ][ ] both

10. experienced and amateur sculptors to showcase their [t][ ][l][e][ ][ ][s].

11. Participants will try to make their artworks as [d][ ][ ][a][b][ ][e]

12. as possible, but [e][v][e][ ][ ][u][a][ ][l][y] the sculptures will

    crumble away.

In each question below, the words can be rearranged to form a sentence. One word doesn't fit in the sentence. Underline the word that doesn't fit.

Example: bus the <u>caught</u> waited the boy for

13. ate on butterfly table our picnic a landed

14. along to the coast walks likes dad my stroll

15. was in speaking not talks public of fan a Melinda

16. my run sore long a after pain were legs

17. play I my concert friend watch the in to listened

Complete the word on the right so that it means the same, or nearly the same, as the word on the left.

Example: kind ⌈c⌉⌈a⌉⌈r⌉⌈i⌉⌈n⌉⌈g⌉

18. doubtful ⌈u⌉⌈ ⌉⌈s⌉⌈ ⌉⌈ ⌉⌈e⌉

19. difficult ⌈c⌉⌈ ⌉⌈m⌉⌈ ⌉⌈l⌉⌈e⌉⌈ ⌉

20. vital ⌈e⌉⌈s⌉⌈ ⌉⌈ ⌉⌈n⌉⌈t⌉⌈ ⌉⌈a⌉⌈l⌉

21. keep ⌈p⌉⌈r⌉⌈ ⌉⌈ ⌉⌈e⌉⌈ ⌉⌈v⌉⌈ ⌉

22. truthful ⌈ ⌉⌈o⌉⌈ ⌉⌈e⌉⌈s⌉⌈ ⌉

72

Find the word that means the opposite, or nearly the opposite, of the word on the left.

Example: **love**   like   annoy   <u>hate</u>   enemy

23. **sweet**   sugary   salt   plain   sour

24. **order**   confused   chaos   busy   destroy

25. **reveal**   conceal   bury   lose   lurk

26. **suspicious**   wary   honest   innocent   trusting

END OF TEST

/ 26

Try this puzzle on for size — it's a great way to practise your **vocabulary** skills.

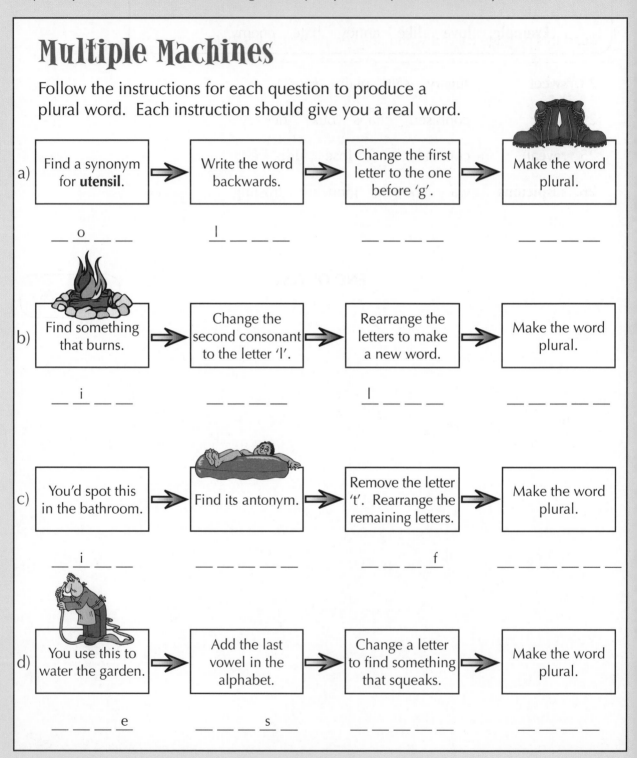

Multiple Machines

Follow the instructions for each question to produce a plural word. Each instruction should give you a real word.

a)

| Find a synonym for **utensil**. | → | Write the word backwards. | → | Change the first letter to the one before 'g'. | → | Make the word plural. |

_ _ o _ _   l _ _ _ _   _ _ _ _   _ _ _ _

b)

| Find something that burns. | → | Change the second consonant to the letter 'l'. | → | Rearrange the letters to make a new word. | → | Make the word plural. |

_ _ i _ _   _ _ _ _   l _ _ _   _ _ _ _ _

c)

| You'd spot this in the bathroom. | → | Find its antonym. | → | Remove the letter 't'. Rearrange the remaining letters. | → | Make the word plural. |

_ _ i _ _   _ _ _ _ _ _   _ _ _ f   _ _ _ _ _

d)

| You use this to water the garden. | → | Add the last vowel in the alphabet. | → | Change a letter to find something that squeaks. | → | Make the word plural. |

_ _ _ e   _ _ _ s _   _ _ _ _   _ _ _ _

You have **10 minutes** to do this test. Work as quickly and accurately as you can.

Read this passage carefully and answer the questions that follow.

Natural History

"Do not touch the dinosaur",
a bright red sign displays;
a prehistoric behemoth*,
lit up in cold white rays.

5   Children walk around in awe,
his giant bones amaze;
but while they gaze upon his face,
he longs for bygone days.

Where once he was a hunter,
10 stalking puny, paltry prey,
now he's just a symbol
a mere touristic display.

A jigsaw from the distant past,
a puzzle we can't solve,
15 a mystery that we fail to crack,
a riddle with no resolve.

His eyes reduced to sockets,
we don't see him in his prime;
his owners turn a profit,
20 but they cannot turn back time.

In some respects we are alike,
neither of us can see
a world that's gone forever now,
save for fossils and debris.

25 One day will we be just the same:
brought out for a curious eye?
Will they describe us from our lives,
or from what our bones imply?

A jigsaw from the distant past,
30 a puzzle they won't solve;
a mystery that they'll fail to crack,
a riddle with no resolve.

* behemoth — *a huge or monstrous creature*

Answer these questions about the text that you've just read.
Circle the letter that matches the correct answer.

1. What is the most likely reason why the sign is "bright red" (line 2)?

    A   Because the dinosaur is the main attraction

    B   Because red is a popular colour

    C   Because it will get people's attention

    D   Because it matches the museum's colour scheme

2. Which of the following statements is false?

    A   The dinosaur is illuminated.

    B   The children are impressed by the dinosaur.

    C   Guests are encouraged to touch the dinosaur.

    D   The owners make money from exhibiting the dinosaur.

3. Which of the following best describes the dinosaur on display?

    A   It was a large, meat-eating dinosaur.

    B   It was a small, meat-eating dinosaur.

    C   It was a large, vegetarian dinosaur.

    D   It is not clear from the text.

4. What does the narrator imply in lines 25-28?

    A   Humans are very similar to dinosaurs.

    B   In the future, humans might be studied and exhibited like dinosaurs.

    C   We'll never know everything about prehistoric times.

    D   Exhibiting dinosaurs in museums is wrong.

5. What is meant by "a riddle with no resolve" (line 16)?

    A   A conundrum that most people struggle to answer

    B   A mystery we have no definite answer to

    C   A puzzle that has more than one right answer

    D   A dilemma with two opposing sides

6. What does "puny" (line 10) mean?

    A   Weak

    B   Dangerous

    C   Swift

    D   Vicious

7. What does "bygone" (line 8) mean?

    A   Prehistoric

    B   Former

    C   Recent

    D   Happier

Find the word that means the same, or nearly the same, as the word on the left.

    Example: **tub**   flask   <u>pot</u>   bottle   glass

---

8. **thrilled**   relieved   disappointed   overwhelmed   elated

9. **halt**   freeze   lull   stop   quieten

10. **lengthen**   develop   shrink   tighten   stretch

11. **massive**   bulky   moderate   substantial   enormous

12. **crave**   greedy   yearn   choose   eager

13. **deserted**   wasted   barren   empty   neglected

Three of the words in each list are linked.
Mark the word that is not related to these three.

Example: red   green   <u>stripy</u>   blue

14. loyal   devoted   clever   trustworthy

15. neglect   defend   patrol   guard

16. chat   talk   scream   gossip

17. island   port   jetty   harbour

18. clock   calendar   sundial   watch

19. amazed   relieved   astounded   shocked

20. complete   conclude   finish   develop

END OF TEST

/ 20

Test 21

You have **10 minutes** to do this test. Work as quickly and accurately as you can.

Read this passage carefully and answer the questions that follow.

An extract from 'The Wouldbegoods'

Then the door of the church tower was ajar, and we all went up; it had always been locked before when we had tried it.

We saw the ringer's loft where the ends of the bell-ropes hang down with long, furry handles to them like great caterpillars, some red, and some blue and white,

5 but we did not pull them. And then we went up to where the bells are, very big and dusty among large dirty beams; and four windows with no glass, only shutters like Venetian blinds*, but they won't pull up. There were heaps of straws and sticks on the window ledges. We think they were owls' nests, but we did not see any owls.

10 Then the tower stairs got very narrow and dark, and we went on up, and we came to a door and opened it suddenly, and it was like being hit in the face, the light was so sudden. And there we were on the top of the tower, which is flat, and people have cut their names on it, and a turret at one corner, and a low wall all round, up and down, like castle battlements. And we looked down and saw

15 the roof of the church, and the leads**, and the church-yard, and our garden, and the Moat House, and the farm, and Mrs Simpkins's cottage, looking very small, and other farms looking like toy things out of boxes, and we saw corn-fields and meadows and pastures. A pasture is not the same thing as a meadow, whatever you may think. And we saw the tops of trees and hedges, looking like the map of

20 the United States, and villages, and a tower that did not look very far away standing by itself on the top of a hill.

E. Nesbit

* Venetian blinds — *a window covering made of horizontal slats that can be raised or lowered*

** leads — *pieces of lead used to cover a roof*

Answer these questions about the text that you've just read.
Circle the letter that matches the correct answer.

1. What are the "great caterpillars" (line 4)?

   A   The bells

   B   The handles of the bell-ropes

   C   The owls' nests

   D   The stairs

2. According to the text, which of the following statements is false?

   A   The bells haven't been cleaned in a long time.

   B   People have etched their names on the roof of the tower.

   C   There are four windows where the bells are kept.

   D   The children ring the bells.

3. According to the text, which of the following statements must be true?

   A   The children see owls' nests in the ringer's loft.

   B   The door to the church tower is often locked.

   C   Mrs Simpkins has a small cottage.

   D   The bell-ropes are all the same colour.

4. Line 17 refers to the farms as "like toy things out of boxes". This suggests:

   A   that the farms are brightly coloured.

   B   that the farms are made from wood.

   C   that the farms are laid out in squares.

   D   that the farms look small from the church tower.

5. Which of the following cannot be seen from the church tower?

    A   A castle

    B   Fields of corn

    C   Hedgerows

    D   Grassy fields

6. What does "ajar" (line 1) mean?

    A   Stuck

    B   Large

    C   Inviting

    D   Open

7. What does "suddenly" (line 11) mean?

    A   Promptly

    B   Steadily

    C   Abruptly

    D   Vigorously

In each question below, the words can be rearranged to form a sentence. One word doesn't fit in the sentence. Underline the word that doesn't fit.

    Example: bus   the   <u>caught</u>   waited   the   boy   for

---

8.   sale   the   purchase   a   charity   school   bake   hosted

9.   clocks   always   time   turn   forgets   back   to   Johan   the

10. eating   peels   always   apples   them   Kirsty   orange   before   her

11. lost   the   bus   he   had   for   coin   money   the

12. meal   my   cooked   eaten   for   my   mum   dinner   favourite

13. prefers   mug   Kristina   of   with   milk   tea   her   splash   a

14. bought   my   tree   hang   I   to   bauble   Christmas   on   present   a

---

Mark the word outside the brackets that has a similar meaning to the words in both sets of brackets.

Example: (circle ring)   (session game)   set   <u>round</u>   oval

---

15. (fry   roast)   (chef   baker)   cook   grill   boil

16. (bus   double-decker) (trainer   instructor)   tutor   car   coach

17. (movie   footage)   (layer   coating)   covering   film   show

18. (blow   waft)   (supporter   admirer)   follower   flap   fan

19. (tire   exhaust)   (pipe   sewer)   drain   gutter   weary

20. (source   origin)   (rummage   dig)   root   foundation   scrape

END OF TEST

/ 20

Test 22

You have **10 minutes** to do this test. Work as quickly and accurately as you can.

> Choose the correct words to complete the passage below.

Flamenco is a traditional art form from southern Spain,

1. ☐ sometimes
   ☐ wholly
   ☐ particularly
   ☐ fairly

the area of Andalucia. Flamenco is

2. ☐ never
   ☐ definitely
   ☐ normally
   ☐ precisely

made up of three parts —

singing, dancing and guitar

3. ☐ played
   ☐ plays
   ☐ play
   ☐ playing

. The dancing is bold and dramatic, with

4. ☐ all
   ☐ frequent
   ☐ lots
   ☐ many

of arm movements and strong facial

5. ☐ looks
   ☐ expressions
   ☐ visions
   ☐ appearance

.

Women

6. ☐ genuinely
   ☐ certainly
   ☐ never
   ☐ typically

wear long dresses and heeled shoes;

men

7. ☐ might
   ☐ have
   ☐ try
   ☐ ought

wear black trousers with a red shirt or sash.

8. ☐ compose
Dancers also   ☐ rehearse   the castanets — instruments that consist of two
                  ☐ play
                  ☐ dance

9. ☐ apart
wooden shells that are clicked   ☐ together
                                 ☐ between .
                                 ☐ closed

10. ☐ important
Flamenco is still an   ☐ special   part of Spanish culture and it is
                      ☐ great
                      ☐ substantial

11. ☐ practised   12. ☐ every
     ☐ watched   ☐ always
     ☐ celebrated   with its own festival in the city of Seville   ☐ often
     ☐ remembered   ☐ during

two years.

Find the word that means the opposite, or nearly the opposite, of the word on the left.

Example: **love**   like   annoy   <u>hate</u>   enemy

13. **after**   around   during   later   before

14. **help**   hinder   aid   ignore   annoy

15. **lit**   broken   burned   soggy   extinguished

16. **forget**   think   speculate   recall   memory

Mark the word outside the brackets that has a similar meaning to the words in both sets of brackets.

Example: (circle ring)   (session game)   set   <u>round</u>   oval

17. (fire dismiss)   (bag satchel)   pouch   sack   expel

18. (cage coop)   (quill felt-tip)   marker   crate   pen

19. (ban forbid)   (pole rail)   refuse   handle   bar

20. (uncooked underdone) (cold icy)   raw   chilly   bleak

21. (sieve drain)   (stress pressure)   strain   tension   wash

Complete the word on the right so that it means the same, or nearly the same, as the word on the left.

Example: kind   [c][a][r][i][n][g]

22. competition   [ ][o][n][ ][ ][s][t]

23. chest   [t][ ][u][ ][ ]

24. trot   [ ][ ][g]

25. refuse   [r][ ][j][ ][ ][t]

26. squander   [ ][a][ ][t][e]

END OF TEST

/ 26

85

Time for a break! These puzzles are a great way to practise your **vocabulary** skills.

Canine Connections

Each member of Young Rover's family has chosen a word.

Solve the clues to work out the word each family member is thinking of. Make sure it's the right word type.

Dad Rover says...
I'm thinking of a noun related to 'trying': __ __ f __ __ __

Cousin Rover says...
I'm thinking of an adverb related to 'afraid': __ e r __ __ __ s __ __

Gran Rover says...
I'm thinking of a noun related to 'tired': __ __ __ a __ s __ __ __ n

Mum Rover says...
I'm thinking of an adjective related to 'athletic': __ __ __ r __ __ __

Uncle Rover's clue is extra tricky because the answer can be pronounced in two different ways. He says... I'm thinking of a verb related to 'descended' that's <u>also</u> a type of bird: __ __ __ __

Word Wheel

Using just the letters in the circle, can you spell the answers to the clues? You can only use each letter once in each word, and every answer must use the letter 'A'.

a verb meaning 'make'   __ __ __ __ __ __ __

a word related to 'forever'   __ __ __ __ __ __ __ __

the opposite of 'earlier'   __ __ __ __ __

an adjective meaning 'graceful'   __ __ __ __ __ __ __

Can you find the nine-letter word? ....

You have **10 minutes** to do this test. Work as quickly and accurately as you can.

Fill in the missing letters to complete the words in the following passage.

1.   Madagascar, a large island off the east coast of Africa, is ⬚⬚m⬚ to

2.   the ring-tailed lemur, a primate with grey f⬚⬚, a long black-and-white

3.   striped tail, and large eyes. Madagascar, along ⬚⬚t⬚ some tiny

4.   islands nearby, is the only place in the ⬚or⬚⬚ where you can

5.   see ring-tailed lemurs in the w⬚⬚l⬚, although you can find them

6.   in zoos across the globe. Some people ⬚h⬚⬚k that the ancestors

7.   of modern-day lemurs may have a⬚r⬚⬚e⬚ in Madagascar by

8.   floating across the ocean on pieces of vegetation millions of years ⬚g⬚,

     but no one knows for sure how they got there.

9.   The d⬚e⬚ of the ring-tailed lemur includes fruit, insects, bark, leaves

10. and flowers. Unlike other sp⬚c⬚e⬚ of lemur who spend

11. most of their time ⬚⬚on⬚⬚t the treetops, ring-tailed lemurs

12. can be spotted fo⬚⬚gi⬚⬚ for food on the ground.

Find the word that means the same, or nearly the same, as the word on the left.

Example: **tub**   flask   <u>pot</u>   bottle   glass

13. **goal**   succeed   effort   ambition   future

14. **quick**   rushed   giddy   jumpy   nimble

15. **carve**   split   chisel   divide   trim

16. **prolong**   extend   grow   unroll   spread

17. **announcement**   comment   review   story   statement

Three of the words in each list are linked.
Mark the word that is not related to these three.

Example: red   green   <u>stripy</u>   blue

18. mountain   hill   valley   peak

19. brisk   lively   sprightly   idle

20. sleepy   snug   comfy   cosy

21. rival   visitor   foe   enemy

22. politician   dentist   pharmacist   doctor

In each question below, the words can be rearranged to form a sentence. One word doesn't fit in the sentence. Underline the word that doesn't fit.

Example: bus   the   <u>caught</u>   waited   the   boy   for

23. cat   really   neighbour's   fight   dislikes   dogs   the   my

24. John   had   to   money   take   dinner   his   forgotten   pick

25. on   Sandra   travel   always   went   the   spring   holiday   in

26. river   they   the   but   bridge   at   had   cross   to   the

END OF TEST

/ 26

Test 24

You have **10 minutes** to do this test. Work as quickly and accurately as you can.

Choose the correct words to complete the passage below.

The high jump is a track and field event where athletes

1. ☐ throw
   ☐ struggle
   ☐ compete   to see
   ☐ beat

who can jump the

2. ☐ highest
   ☐ longest
   ☐ forwards
   ☐ backwards

over a horizontal bar. Each

3. ☐ worker
   ☐ helper
   ☐ participant
   ☐ friend

tries to clear the jump without dislodging the bar, which is raised slightly higher after

4. ☐ last
   ☐ first
   ☐ all   round. In the first half of the 20th-century, most
   ☐ each

5. ☐ spectators
   ☐ compete
   ☐ spectate   would
   ☐ competitors

clear the bar by jumping forwards and kicking their legs in a scissor movement.

One of the most

6. ☐ best
   ☐ rich
   ☐ famous   high jumpers is Dick Fosbury, who won
   ☐ strong

an Olympic gold medal in 1968. He

7. ☐ pioneered
   ☐ opened
   ☐ saw   a new technique, which
   ☐ watched

8. ☐ used
   ☐ involved
   ☐ mean   jumping over the bar backwards, arching in the air, and
   ☐ taught

9. ☐ drop
   ☐ hitting
   ☐ fall
   ☐ landing

on his back. This method was made possible by new,

10. ☐ harder
    ☐ relaxed   landing mats.
    ☐ softer
    ☐ older

It became known as the Fosbury Flop, and is the main

11. ☐ behaviour
    ☐ technique
    ☐ skill   used by
    ☐ attitude

professional high jumpers, including the

12. ☐ customary
    ☐ current
    ☐ tomorrow   world record holder, Javier
    ☐ today

Sotomayor, who successfully cleared a height of 2.45 m in 1993.

In each question below, the words can be rearranged to form a sentence.
One word doesn't fit in the sentence. Underline the word that doesn't fit.

Example: bus   the   <u>caught</u>   waited   the   boy   for

13. Bradley   part   triathlon   competed   in   took   recently   a

14. and   so   collected   America   from   his   stamps   sister   George

15. the   warmed   and   fire   blaze   crackled   the   room   log

16. spaghetti   messy   I   ate   a   I   eater   when   am   eat

Three of the words in each list are linked.
Mark the word that is not related to these three.

Example: red   green   <u>stripy</u>   blue

17. stable   cottage   kennel   sty

18. gorilla   chimpanzee   baboon   koala

19. food   delicious   flavourful   tasty

20. boat   yacht   barge   surfboard

21. thought   decided   questioned   speculated

Mark the word outside the brackets that has a similar meaning to the words in both sets of brackets.

Example: (circle   ring)   (session   game)   set   <u>round</u>   oval

22. (tin   jar)   (could   may)   might   can   bottle

23. (exist   survive)   (stay   reside)   lodge   live   breathe

24. (opinion   belief)   (scene   panorama)   view   thought   sight

25. (chill   refrigerate)   (fashionable   stylish)   frosty   popular   cool

26. (level   smooth)   (apartment   residence)   housing   flat   even

END OF TEST

/ 26

You have **10 minutes** to do this test. Work as quickly and accurately as you can.

Read this passage carefully and answer the questions that follow.

The Cliffs

They sing of the grandeur of cliffs inland,
But the cliffs of the ocean are truly grand;
And I long to wander and dream and doubt
Where the cliffs by the ocean run out and out.

5 To the northward far as the eye can reach
Are sandhill, boulder, and sandy beach;
But southward rises the track for me,
Where the cliffs by the ocean run out to sea.

Friends may be gone in the morning fair,
10 But the cliffs by the ocean are always there;
Lovers may leave when the wind is chill,
But the cliffs by the ocean are steadfast still.

They watch the sea and they ward the land,
And they warn the ships from the treacherous sand;
15 And I sadly think in the twilight hour
What I might have been had I known my power.

Where the smoke-cloud blurs and the white sails fill,
They point the ships to keep seaward still;
And I think — Ah, me! — and I think — Ah, me!
20 Of the wreck I'd saved had I kept to sea.

Oh! the cliffs are old and the cliffs are sad,
And they know me sane, while men deem me mad.
Oh! the cliffs are firm and the cliffs are strong,
And they know me right, while men deem me wrong.

25 And I sometimes think in the dawning grey,
I am old as they, I am old as they;
And I think, I think that in field and town
My spirit shall live till the cliffs come down.

Henry Lawson

Answer these questions about the text that you've just read.
Circle the letter that matches the correct answer.

1. According to the narrator, what advantage do the cliffs have over friends?

   A   Cliffs are easier to find than friends.

   B   Cliffs are unaffected by the weather.

   C   Cliffs are grander than friends.

   D   Cliffs are more dependable than friends.

2. The narrator says that the cliffs "ward the land" (line 13). This means:

   A   they watch the land.

   B   they block the land.

   C   they protect the land.

   D   they ignore the land.

3. What is implied by the narrator on lines 19-20?

   A   That he is watching the cliffs from his ship

   B   That his ship sank

   C   That the cliffs saved him from being shipwrecked

   D   That he would rather be at sea than on land

4. Which of the following is not mentioned in the text?

   A   Sand dunes

   B   A beach

   C   A field

   D   A forest

5. Why do you think sailors might be grateful to the cliffs?

    A   They are interesting to look at while sailing.

    B   They alert them to the land ahead.

    C   They channel air into their ship's sails.

    D   They are a good inspiration for song writing.

6. What does "grandeur" (line 1) mean?

    A   Appearance

    B   Magnificence

    C   Presence

    D   Convenience

7. What does "treacherous" (line 14) mean?

    A   Daunting

    B   Alarming

    C   Ominous

    D   Dangerous

Complete the word on the right so that it means the same, or nearly the same, as the word on the left.

Example: kind [c][a][r][i][n][g]

---

8. complete   [ ][i][ ][ ][s][h]

9. admiration [ ][e][ ][p][ ][c][ ]

10. movement [m][ ][ ][i][ ][n]

                Test 25

11. new   ☐ r ☐ s h

12. follow   p ☐ r ☐ u ☐

13. real   g ☐ ☐ u i ☐ e

Find the word that means the opposite, or nearly the opposite, of the word on the left.

Example: **love**   like   annoy   <u>hate</u>   enemy

---

14. **lift**   carry   collapse   drop   place

15. **best**   top   inferior   average   worst

16. **ugly**   handsome   gentle   neat   unattractive

17. **simple**   easy   tedious   intricate   crucial

18. **glad**   empty   isolated   dim   sorrowful

19. **clumsy**   clever   silly   deft   witty

20. **separate**   combine   strengthen   collection   fix

END OF TEST

/ 20

Have a break and give these puzzles a go.

Monster Rhymes

Fill in the gaps to complete the poem.
The missing words rhyme with the
last word on the previous line.

*The rhyming word
should make sense
in the sentence.*

Creature in the Dark

This poem's quite creepy, so beware —

Read on only if you _____!

Once, in the dead of the night,

I had a most terrible _____:

I saw a creature, tall and hairy,

Not a troll, but just as _____.

It slowly crept around the door,

Its footsteps thudded on the _____.

Its chest heaved and its eyes glared,

Its sharp yellow teeth were _____.

It lumbered over towards my bed,

A claw raised above its _____.

In terror, I began to scream,

Hoping this was just a _____.

....

....

↳ *Finish it off!*

Sound It Out

The missing words in each of the sentences
below <u>sound</u> the same but are <u>spelled</u> differently.

Fill the gaps to complete each sentence.

1. The _____ stirred the cauldron, _____ contained frogs and newts.

2. The wind that _____ was so cold that it turned my fingers _____.

3. Mum sat down with a _____ of cake for a bit of _____ and quiet.

4. The box had ten chocolates. I _____ two — then there were _____.

5. After Elle had _____ the bell, she _____ her hands nervously.

You have **10 minutes** to do this test. Work as quickly and accurately as you can.

Fill in the missing letters to complete the words in the following passage.

1.   Silk is a delicate, shiny f_b r__, which is most often used to

2.   make l_x_r_ou_ clothes and furnishings. However, silk

3.   has some more p_ac_i_al uses too: it was traditionally

     used to make parachutes and has even been used in space vessels.

4.   _n_ik_ some materials, such as cotton, silk isn't made from

5.   plants. In__e_d, it's made from the cocoons of the silkworm.

6.   Silkworms are white caterpillars t_a_ spin cocoons made of soft

7.   fibres. These fibres are gathered and spun into silk t_re__s.

8.   The first civilization to u__ silk was reportedly ancient China,

9.   and it quickly became a _re_i_us item due to the length

10. of t___ it took to make, and its smooth texture. Today, China

11. is the _ar_e_t producer of silk, and it's estimated that the

12. silk industry provides jobs for a_p r_x im_t_l y

     one million Chinese workers.

Mark the word outside the brackets that has a similar meaning to the words in both sets of brackets.

Example: (circle   ring)   (session   game)   set   <u>round</u>   oval

13. (stick   cane)   (workforce   employees)   staff   squad   pole

14. (happy   cheerful) (bright   summery)   delighted   cloudless   sunny

15. (buttery   creamy) (wealthy   well-off)   affluent   rich   heavy

16. (crops   harvest)   (make   create)   goods   construct   produce

17. (peace   unity)   (tune   melody)   harmony   chord   accord

Three of the words in each list are linked.
Mark the word that is not related to these three.

Example: red   green   <u>stripy</u>   blue

18. café   kitchen   diner   restaurant

19. dig   shovel   soil   scoop

20. flock   swarm   herd   couple

21. mundane   exciting   normal   ordinary

22. marble   ruby   diamond   emerald

Find the word that means the same, or nearly the same, as the word on the left.

Example: **tub**   flask   <u>pot</u>   bottle   glass

23. **protect**   lock   assure   support   defend

24. **tumble**   skid   fall   slip   accident

25. **destroy**   demolish   vandalise   damage   hurt

26. **unhygienic**   marked   stained   dirty   spoiled

END OF TEST

/ 26

You have **10 minutes** to do this test. Work as quickly and accurately as you can.

Choose the correct words to complete the passage below.

The saxophone is a musical instrument that is played

1. ☐ with
   ☐ by
   ☐ as
   ☐ of

blowing into

a mouthpiece and pressing different keys to

2. ☐ produce
   ☐ present
   ☐ show
   ☐ discover

different notes. It has a

3. ☐ what
   ☐ which
   ☐ where
   ☐ who

curved body, on the keys are found, and a large hole for the sound to

4. ☐ lead
   ☐ fall
   ☐ exit
   ☐ withdraw

. It was invented in the early 1840s by a Belgian instrument maker called

5. ☐ wanted
   ☐ hope
   ☐ imagined
   ☐ dream

Adolphe Sax, who to create an instrument that

6. ☐ combined
   ☐ combining
   ☐ combine
   ☐ combination

7. ☐ of
   ☐ in
   ☐ that
   ☐ to

the quick notes a woodwind instrument, like a clarinet, and the power of a

brass instrument, like a trumpet. The reed in the mouthpiece,

8. ☐ also
   ☐ while
   ☐ along
   ☐ and

with the

metal body of the saxophone, allowed him to merge these

9. ☐ shapes
   ☐ ideas
   ☐ qualities .
   ☐ parts

Saxophones were first used in military bands, but they are

10. ☐ current
    ☐ now
    ☐ present   more
    ☐ past

commonly associated

11. ☐ by
    ☐ from
    ☐ with   jazz music. Jazz music can feature complicated
    ☐ to

solos, which allow the saxophone player to demonstrate their

12. ☐ musical
    ☐ intelligence
    ☐ performance .
    ☐ talent

Complete the word on the right so that it means the opposite,
or nearly the opposite, of the word on the left.

Example: start   [e][n][d]

13. soft   [c][ ][ ][n][c][h][ ]

14. deflate   [s][w][ ][ ][ ][l]

15. release   [t][r][ ][ ][ ]

16. disheartened   [h][ ][p][e][ ][ ][l]

Mark the word outside the brackets that has a similar meaning to the words in both sets of brackets.

Example: (circle ring) (session game)   set   <u>round</u>   oval

17. (barn shed)   (steady secure)   stable   shelter   solid

18. (clever intelligent)(sting prickle)   bookish   smart   pain

19. (draw stalemate) (link connect)   tie   bond   balance

20. (knob lever)   (manage control)   handgrip   govern   handle

21. (fort castle)   (hold retain)   preserve   tower   keep

Three of the words in each list are linked.
Mark the word that is not related to these three.

Example: red   green   <u>stripy</u>   blue

22. petty   picky   choosy   fussy

23. burrow   nest   cage   den

24. writer   journalist   reporter   article

25. snooker   tennis   cricket   darts

26. roomy   empty   sizeable   spacious

END OF TEST

/ 26

You have **10 minutes** to do this test. Work as quickly and accurately as you can.

Read this passage carefully and answer the questions that follow.

Groundhog Day

For centuries, people have attempted to predict the weather based on animal behaviour. Old wives' tales suggest that cows, frogs, spiders and ants are just some of the animals to keep an eye on if you suspect that bad weather is round the corner. Advances in science and technology have led to more sophisticated methods of

5   weather forecasting, but despite this, the people of Punxsutawney, Pennsylvania still put their faith in something quite unusual.

Since 1887, a succession of groundhogs* named Punxsutawney Phil have been watched every 2nd February. People gather to watch Phil emerge from his burrow after winter hibernation. When Phil emerges, one of two things will happen. If he

10 surfaces on a cloudy day, it means that winter is nearly over and spring is coming. If, however, he sees his own shadow, Phil supposedly scurries back into his burrow, and people believe that winter will last for six more weeks.

The origin of the groundhog legend remains undetermined, but it is commonly believed to have derived from the Christian festival of Candlemas. If the weather on

15 Candlemas was bright and clear, wintry weather would continue, but if the weather was cloudy or rainy then spring was just around the corner.

It's not just Pennsylvanians who celebrate weather-predicting rodents: Ohio has Buckeye Chuck, New York has Staten Island Chuck, and Ontario, Canada has Wiarton Willie. But it's Phil who remains the star. Crowds of up to 40 000 people

20 flock to Pennsylvania to catch sight of him, and in recent years his predictions have been broadcast online to allow others to share in the excitement.

Despite his popularity, Phil's accuracy has come into question. Some of his supporters claim that he has an accuracy of 80%, but some researchers have declared that this is more likely to be around 40%. However, there's one thing that

25 remains certain — Groundhog Day is here to stay!

* groundhog — *a medium-sized brown rodent native to North America*

1. Which of the following best describes Groundhog Day?
    A   A Christian festival
    B   A much-loved annual event
    C   An old wives' tale
    D   A reliable way of predicting the weather

2. According to researchers, Punxsutawney Phil:
    A   is correct 80% of the time.
    B   is correct 60% of the time.
    C   is more likely to be correct than incorrect.
    D   is more likely to be incorrect than correct.

3. Which of the following statements is true?
    A   If February 2nd is a sunny day, Punxsutawney Phil predicts a longer winter.
    B   If February 2nd is a cloudy day, Punxsutawney Phil predicts a longer winter.
    B   If February 2nd is a sunny day, Punxsutawney Phil predicts a shorter winter.
    D   If Punxsutawney Phil scurries into his burrow, he predicts a shorter winter.

4. Which of the following rodents is the most celebrated?
    A   Wiarton Willie
    B   Buckeye Chuck
    C   Punxsutawney Phil
    D   Staten Island Chuck

5. Which of the following is not mentioned in the text?

    A   Where in Pennsylvania the celebrations take place.

    B   When the first Groundhog Day was celebrated in Punxsutawney.

    C   What day of the year Groundhog Day is celebrated.

    D   Why Groundhog Day is so popular in Pennsylvania.

6. What does "sophisticated" mean (line 4)?

    A   Refined

    B   Reliable

    C   Widespread

    D   Accepted

7. What does "undetermined" mean (line 13)?

    A   Popular

    B   Unproven

    C   Well-known

    D   Secretive

Three of the words in each list are linked.
Mark the word that is not related to these three.

Example: red   green   stripy   blue

8. dust   stain   mud   dirt

9. bag   box   bin   suitcase

10. fun   enthusiastic   keen   eager

11. chase   charge   blame   accuse

12. floor   ceiling   wall   room

13. help   assist   advice   support

14. boast   brag   gloat   succeed

Mark the word outside the brackets that has a similar meaning to the words in both sets of brackets.

Example: (circle   ring)   (session   game)   set   <u>round</u>   oval

15. (slant   tilt)   (hint   suggestion)   clue   tip   lean

16. (insect   gnat)   (float   glide)   fly   moth   sail

17. (clever   smart)   (dazzling   vivid)   wise   sparkling   bright

18. (wash   bathe)   (rain   drizzle)   flood   shower   sink

19. (story   text)   (reserve   hire)   rent   novel   book

20. (knife   spoon)   (split   junction)   crossing   fork   utensil

END OF TEST

/ 20

Time for a break! These puzzles are a great way to practise your **spelling** skills.

Aliens are Landing!

A space station has intercepted a message about an alien invasion.

Fill in the letters that are given to you, then find the missing letters to decipher the message.

W |

△ | △ | ~ | ~
| | L |

□ | @ | @ | □ | # | ~
T | | | | |

@ | * | ◉
| | E

◉ | □ | ○ | @ | * | ~ | △ | ⊐ | ⊔ | ∧
| A | | | | | | | |

◇ | Ζ
| N

@ | < | ◉ | ∧ | / | □ | ∨
| | | | | | .

Letter Lasso

Each of the words below has at least one letter missing. Add the missing letters to the box, and then use them to finish a phrase a cowboy or girl might say.

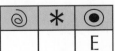 c o n s c i u s   h a n s o m

 o p o t u n i t y   r y t h m

 o c c u r e d   e n v i r o m e n t

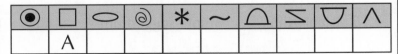

Phrase:
_ _ w _ y _ a _ t _ _ _ _!

108

Test 29

You have **10 minutes** to do this test. Work as quickly and accurately as you can.

Fill in the missing letters to complete the words in the following passage.

1. Denmark's capital city, Copenhagen, is a ☐☐sy European

2. hub with over half a million in☐☐bi☐a☐ts,

3. but it has had a turbulent h☐st☐☐y.

4. In the early 1700s, Copenhagen was s☐r☐☐k by the plague,

5. and the city lost around a third of its p☐☐ul☐t☐on.

6. A few years later, a fire de☐t☐oye☐ over a quarter of the

7. city, which left many citizens wi☐ho☐☐ homes. In the

8. early 1800s, Copenhagen was ☐tt☐ck☐d by British forces

9. and parts of the city had to be r☐bu☐☐t.

10. Nowadays, Copenhagen is a lot more p☐a☐ef☐☐,

11. and it ☐☐gul☐r☐☐ features on lists of

    "cities with the happiest residents". It also tops the polls as one

12. of the best places in the world in which to ☐☐v☐.

Three of the words in each list are linked.
Mark the word that is not related to these three.

Example: red   green   <u>stripy</u>   blue

13. rocky   grainy   gritty   sandy

14. foot   wing   paw   hoof

15. writing   paper   paragraph   text

16. likely   true   right   correct

17. frost   ice   snow   slippery

Mark the word outside the brackets that has a similar meaning to the words in both sets of brackets.

Example: (circle ring)   (session game)   set   <u>round</u>   oval

18. (pat touch)   (faucet spout)   tap   nozzle   stroke

19. (thin slender)(minor insignificant)   trivial   slight   dainty

20. (chime toll)   (hoop loop)   circle   ring   sound

21. (decay rot)   (indulge pamper)   mould   treat   spoil

22. (plank panel)(lodge rent)   live   board   slat

Complete the word on the right so that it means the opposite, or nearly the opposite, of the word on the left.

Example: start [e][n][d]

23. blame   [f][ ][r][ ][ ][v][e]

24. meagre   [a][m][ ][ ][e]

25. worthless   [v][ ][l][ ][ ][b][l][e]

26. tanned   [a][s][ ][e][ ]

END OF TEST

/ 26

Test 29

You have **10 minutes** to do this test. Work as quickly and accurately as you can.

Read this passage carefully and answer the questions that follow.

An abridged extract from 'The Lay of the Land'

Lately I found a den of young foxes within barking distance of the house, but along a
stony ridge on the adjoining farm. No one would believe in the number of foxes (or
the number of times I have counted the same fox) here on the farm [...]

5   One day, as we were sitting down to a noon dinner, I heard the hens squawk, and
out I tore. The fox had a big black hen and was making off for the woods. I made
after the fox. There is a sharp ridge back of the henyard, which was thickly covered
with stump sprouts and slashings*. The fox took to the ridge. From the house to the
henyard it is all downhill, and I wanted that hen. She weighed a good eight pounds,
— a load for any fox, — and what with her squawking and flopping, the tangle of
10   brush and the steep hillside, it is small wonder that just short of the top I fell upon
her, to the great sorrow of the fox, who held on until I was within reach of him [...]

a study of the lay of the land hereabout reveals a real fox community overlying
our farm community like some faint tracing. We humans possess the land by day
and the foxes keep to their dens; the foxes possess the land at night and we humans
15   take to our dens.

One of the high roads of the foxes runs across the farm. Foxes, like men, are
more or less mechanical in their coming and going. They will move within certain
well-defined boundaries, running certain definite routes; crossing the stream at a
particular ford** every time, travelling this ridge and not that, leaving the road at this
20   point, and swinging off in just such a circle through the swamp.

Dallas Lore Sharp

* slashings — *woody remains*
** ford — *shallow part of a stream*

Answer these questions about the text that you've just read.
Circle the letter that matches the correct answer.

1. The fox den is described as being "within barking distance of the house" (line 1). This suggests:

   A   that the foxes are unruly.

   B   that the foxes are young.

   C   that the foxes are close.

   D   that the foxes are hungry.

2. What causes the narrator to go outside?

   A   The narrator sees the fox.

   B   The hens start making noise.

   C   The fox starts barking.

   D   The narrator sees the hen.

3. According to the text, which of the following statements cannot be true?

   A   Foxes are mostly nocturnal animals.

   B   Foxes behave unpredictably.

   C   There are lots of foxes on the farm.

   D   A fox's home is called a den.

4. Which of the following is not given as a reason why the fox didn't escape with the hen?

   A   The hen was heavy.

   B   The hen was struggling.

   C   The terrain was difficult.

   D   The fox was trapped.

5. According to the text, at what time does the fox make off with the hen?

    A   Morning

    B   Midday

    C   Evening

    D   Midnight

6. What does "adjoining" (line 2) mean?

    A   Separate

    B   Remote

    C   Neighbouring

    D   Wooden

7. What does "boundaries" (line 18) mean?

    A   Streams

    B   Confines

    C   Ridges

    D   Routes

Find the word that means the opposite, or nearly the opposite, of the word on the left.

    Example: **love**   like   annoy   <u>hate</u>   enemy

---

8. **catch**   soar grab throw receive

9. **bright**   light muddy dim damp

10. **boring**   easy interesting detailed complicated

11. **belittle**   polite flatter convince ignore

12. **crease**   separate bend smooth straight

13. **significant**   idle minor small secondary

In each question below, the words can be rearranged to form a sentence. One word doesn't fit in the sentence. Underline the word that doesn't fit.

Example: bus   the   <u>caught</u>   waited   the   boy   for

---

14. garden kittens runs our cat through always the

15. last the busy yesterday was very weekend supermarket

16. over trip I wrist sprained I my fell when

17. hammer Barney garden on shed own built the his

18. bell when noon off the leaves at everyone rings

19. jam I on my butter put scone bake and

20. made cup I of leave I before tea drink a

END OF TEST

/ 20

You have **10 minutes** to do this test. Work as quickly and accurately as you can.

Choose the correct words to complete the passage below.

Have you ever
1. ☐ heard
☐ hearing
☐ listened
☐ listening
someone refer to the stairs as 'apples and

pears', or the phone as the 'dog and bone'?
2. ☐ Those
☐ These
☐ Then
☐ This
type of language use is

called rhyming slang, and it's
3. ☐ consider
☐ told
☐ believe
☐ thought
to have originated in the East End

of London in the 19th century. No one knows its
4. ☐ wide
☐ specify
☐ exact
☐ detail
origins, but one

suggestion is that criminals may have
5. ☐ invented
☐ tried
☐ discovered
☐ seen
a rhyming code to prevent the

police from understanding what they were saying.
6. ☐ Another
☐ Extra
☐ More
☐ Further
theory is that rhyming

slang was developed by street traders so that they could talk in front of customers without being understood.

7. ☐ was
   ☐ once
   ☐ needed
   ☐ used

Although it   to be popular, rhyming slang has now

8. ☐ quite
   ☐ mostly
   ☐ little
   ☐ some

fallen out of use, particularly amongst young people.

9. ☐ Because
   ☐ However
   ☐ Whilst
   ☐ Of

, there are

10. ☐ examples
    ☐ types
    ☐ some
    ☐ number

new slang terms that have emerged relatively

11. ☐ recently
    ☐ late
    ☐ closely
    ☐ often

— 'Scooby Doo' can mean 'clue' and 'Barney Rubble' can mean

12. ☐ 'collapse'
    ☐ 'difficult'
    ☐ 'danger'   .
    ☐ 'trouble'

Mark the word outside the brackets that has a similar meaning to the words in both sets of brackets.

Example: (circle ring) (session game)   set   <u>round</u>   oval

---

13. (best most)   (T-shirt sweater)   jumper   top   first

14. (well fountain)   (jump leap)   spring   geyser   skip

15. (belong conform) (healthy strong)   exercise match   fit

16. (dog pup)   (chase harass)   mutt   bother   hound

17. (gap hole)   (start beginning)   opening cavity   launch

Three of the words in each list are linked.
Mark the word that is not related to these three.

Example: red   green   stripy   blue

18. smear   rub   dirt   wipe

19. day   October   month   year

20. lyrics   rock   classical   pop

21. man   woman   couple   child

22. town   country   village   city

Find the word that means the same, or nearly the same, as the word on the left.

Example: **tub**   flask   pot   bottle   glass

23. **rare**   valuable   uncommon   new   beautiful

24. **creative**   imaginative   talent   clever   gifted

25. **errand**   dutiful   responsible   task   work

26. **entertain**   satisfy   amuse   amaze   intrigue

END OF TEST

/ 26